THE

Doubleday & Company, Inc., Garden City, New York, 1953

COFFEE TRAIN

By Margarethe Erdahl Shank

Line Drawings by Reisie Lonette

This is the story of Grandma Henrickson, to whom the unseen was always as real as the seen. All the characters were, or are, living people.

The names of all characters are fictitious, and the place name Grand Prairie is fictitious.

LIBRARY OF CONGRESS CATALOG CARD NUMBER 53–9129

Copyright, 1953, by Margarethe Erdahl Shank
All Rights Reserved
Printed in the United States
At the Country Life Press, Garden City, N.Y.

Designed by Diana Klemin

The Coffee Train

1

Evening   The prevailing northwest wind, blowing fresh and eager from the plains of Saskatchewan, was the voice of Dakota. Through long June days when twilight lingered like a fondling hand, it bent the wheat fields into shimmering ribbons of green and shadowed gray. During the clear golden days of Indian summer it rustled its warning in the cottonwoods, bare now except for a few wrinkled brown leaves hanging to stiff branches like forgotten sparrows.

Then one November night a shrill, hollow whining mocked at the moon-whitened stubble fields; and winter stormed down from Canada to tear at human shelters and shape the beaten snow into sculptured mountains and valleys.

But even on such a night as this Mrs. Zemke's cow gave milk. And even on such a night as this Grandma Henrickson looked up from her knitting to the carved clock upon the wall and signaled to me to fetch the evening's supply

9 of milk.

A hot coal sizzled and sang in the firebox. The wind made an experimental descent into the chimney and ran screaming to the back of the house, shaking the storm door on the entry back of the kitchen. It did not seem the sort of night to send anyone out, let alone an eight-year-old child, but Grandpa was a man—a Norwegian man—and they did not set out upon women's errands, as Grandma's patient but determined look seemed to say. She handed me the quart pail. Monsey, our black and white cat with Boston terrier markings, stirred irritably as I reached beyond him to fetch my overshoes drying behind the range; and then he curled again into his warm cocoon of sleep.

I wound a bright scarf around my throat, fastened on a knitted cap with a pompon over each ear, and pulled on a suede-lined coat. Grandma, busy setting a batch of bread to rise, peered at me from around the pantry door. "Be careful!" she cautioned. "The snow is drifting high." I wished to protest the need for fetching milk on such a stormy night; but though her eyes were serene and kind, Bestemor's chin was small and firm. Also I had reason to remember a night I did not go, fretting over the evening errand.

"Javel," she had said, reaching up into the stair well beyond the kitchen, to fetch her coat and cap. "Very well, I'll do it."

"I'll go! I'll go, Bestemor!" I had cried.

She pulled the knitted cap over her neatly parted hair. "Even the wind sings a steadier song than you. Fetch the bucket," she said. So I had heard the doors close behind her, and the squeak of her shuffling steps upon the hard-packed snow. There was no sound in the quiet house but dropping embers in the kitchen range and the hollow ticking of the clock on the wall. Should I run after her and meet her in the snow-banked lane? And then at last I heard her steps upon the walk below the window.

"Take the bucket," she said as I held the door open for her.

"What happened, *Bestemor?*" I cried.

"I fell and spilled the milk on myself. So *myrkt* it was, so dark it was, I could not see the path across the drifted snow and caught my foot in the top of the gate." Yet when she had washed the frozen milk off her coat, she spoke of it no more and set about the evening's tasks as though she had not been outdoors and the milk was in the pantry crock.

So now I stood this November night with my mittened hand upon the doorknob, the aluminum pail with its tight windproof lid slung across my arm. "It's terrible outside. Hear the wind!" I said.

Grandma came out of the pantry. "Never, never," she admonished, "say the weather is bad! God sends the weather, and who are we to pass judgment, even on such a night as this?" I had to smile, and then I drew the door shut, groping my way across the storm shanty to the outer doors. When I had fought with the racing wind and succeeded in fastening the storm-door latch, there remained nothing more to do but place one searching foot in front of the other in the general direction of the Zemke cow.

Lanterns there were, but not to be placed in the wool-mittened hands of a small child. Yet the same instinct, perhaps, that enabled the Vikings once to head sharp-nosed 11 ships across the tossing North Sea directed the feet of a child down snowy lanes and past the rapacious clutch of barbed-wire fences and protruding shrubs.

Once I reached our gate and lost the lonely comfort of a patch of light shining through the frosted kitchen window, our unlighted street became an avenue of terror. To the left stretched a mile-long field, where buried grains awaited the resurrection of spring. Beyond the field was the cemetery, where the departed of Grand Prairie lay, awaiting the resurrections of the Catholics and the Protestants. The cemetery always seemed to move closer those stormy nights; and the same snow that had just swirled over the graves and headstones, I felt sure, was now stinging my face with hypodermic thrusts.

Caught in a fence skirting the Rekve Store's deserted livery stable, a torn newspaper flapped briskly in the wind, freed itself, and danced crazily before my halting steps. A distant street light, suspended loosely on a wire between two posts, swung like a trapeze artist and threw long drifting shadows across the banked snow. Down the near railroad tracks, where hobos camped in summer, the stiff cottonwoods bordering the Zemke yard scraped and rasped their waving branches. I raced around the jet-black corner of the Zemke house and pounded on the back door.

"Gum in, gum in." In her dimly lighted kitchen Mrs. Zemke stirred a pot of soup steaming on the range. "Zit down, zit down," she commanded, pointing over her thin shoulder with a long wooden spoon to indicate a worn, straight-back chair against the brown wood-paneled wall. The house always smelled of onions and garlic and long-past meals. The kerosene lamp on top of the warming

oven flickered uncertainly in the drafty air. A dingy patch of cloth was stretched across the top of a milk can waiting in the sink. I could think of nothing to say to the spare, silent woman, who stirred her kettle of soup firmly.

Then a loud stamping of feet and a rattling of buckets outside in the entry announced Mr. Zemke's current victory over his cow. He threw the door open with a violent push of his hand and shouted under his bobbing mustache, "Well, well, girlie! Tonight again you ketched me up, you ketched me up!" Mrs. Zemke, still silent and sober-faced, held the patch of cloth firmly in place with her sharp-knuckled hands, while he poured the foaming milk from his pail. The too sweet odor of fresh milk mingled companionably with the permanent odor of onions and garlic.

"Your pucket, blease? She is ready?" The old man took my aluminum pail and held it for his wife to fill. I drew six cents out of my mittened hand.

The old man smiled. *"Danke schoen,"* he said. "Run fast now, girlie, *mit* the cover on!" He shook his head. "She iss a real storm coming. A real storm!" The old man held the back door open for me until I reached the corner of his house. Again I was in the unleashed violence of the winter night. Yet the return was always easier, with the street light at my back; and between gusts of driving snow the light that was Grandma's kitchen window beckoned like a wavering beacon. There was one more mortally dreaded spot, the back-door sidewalk and steps, where the wind tore with renewed violence as though loath to part with its sport, and where the dark was always darker until I could wrench open the storm door.

14   Grandma met me in the entry. "I am glad you are back,"

she said. She spoke in her beloved Norwegian, as she led me into the kitchen. Grandpa, leaning over the kitchen table enjoying a book, looked up and smiled. Monsey stirred in his blankets by the winking grate. I took off my icy wraps and hung them in the stair well next to the pantry door.

"I did the dishes," remarked Grandma, as though to reward me for the evening's chore. "But are your lessons done?"

"Only a few arithmetic problems left," I lied.

Grandpa looked up and smiled. "And how many are a few tonight?" he asked.

"Thirteen left," I replied.

"Thirteen!" he exclaimed. "How many have you done?"

"Two." I sat down beside him at the table.

"Ole," said Grandma, drawing her rocker close to the kitchen range, "don't torment her. Do you not know arithmetic makes her head ache?" Grandma's steel knitting needles began to click. "Gyda, her mother, was also that way."

Grandpa pulled a handkerchief from his pocket and began to polish his dime-store glasses. "It's too bad I cannot help you," he sympathized, slipping the glasses on his high-bridged nose and easing the silvered frames upon his ears. "But you see I cannot, as one who does his adding in Norwegian." He ducked his head behind a newspaper.

The teakettle toward the back of the big range hummed experimentally, and then burst into a piping song. Down in the basement the coal in the bins slid down with an echoing rumble. I hoped Grandpa would not send me
15 down the dark cellar steps to bring up apples stored in a

box by the furnace. The storm window at my back rattled in the rising wind. "I wish Aunt Gudrun were coming home tonight!" I cried.

"I advised her not to try it," said Grandma. "When choir practice is over, she'll go home with Tina and your Uncle Thorvald. If she's with them, we need not worry."

Grandpa was chuckling to himself. "Listen to this, Guro," he said. "Here is a story of how a ladies' aid of a certain church financed a new building by violating all the principles of Christianity."

"What do you mean?" Grandma asked guardedly.

"Oh, they gave banquets and *lutefisk* suppers and socials in a spirit of most outrageous and violent competition."

Bestemor's knitting needles clicked like icicles falling to a sidewalk. "But without them—the women of our churches—the buildings might never have been built." As the wind hooted down the chimney and the lignite coal in the range snapped and crackled and fell into the dark oblivion of the ash box, Grandpa read about the rivalry, the petty animosity, and the staggering amount of competition which often inspired the women of the church to bake the best cake and brew the richest coffee for church socials. When the satire cut too deeply, Grandma began to rock with energy. Yet cooking ladies' aid coffee, I thought, was an achievement of no mean ability, for among Scandinavians only amber perfection itself was the goal; and if the women of our church had ever let their hair down sufficiently to be caught saying the *Skaal* of their more uninhibited ancestors, it would have been with coffee cups. Grandpa's reading droned on. Grandma 16 nodded over her knitting. Suddenly she came to with a start. "Do you want me to put the coffeepot on, Ole?" she asked.

Grandpa paused long enough in his reading to nod, and Grandma laid her knitting upon the homemade settee under the clock, took the coffeepot from the back of the stove, and placed it toward the front. A short, slightly bent little woman, she stood by the warming fire with a look of infinite patience about her mouth. The clock on the east wall chimed nine times, taking long indrawn breaths between each gong. "Can I wind it?" I begged.

"We'll see," she said. Many years and six children had taught her the wisdom of never promising a child something unless the commitment were necessary. Then I remembered that the Castoria bottle always stood back of one of the ornate scallops on the side of the face of the clock, and decided not to press the matter further.

With the air of one who has known a cup of coffee and a companionable sharing of cookies and sweets to mend many an ill, Grandma called us to the table.

"No milk again?" she asked me.

"*Nei, tak.* No, thanks," I said, since I had begun to dislike milk, even when I wasn't carrying it home. I slipped my unfinished problems into the arithmetic book.

When the coffee dishes had been carried into the pantry and neatly stacked for tomorrow's doing, Grandma took the devotion book from the shelf under the clock. Somewhat reluctantly Grandpa laid down the paper he had been reading, straightened his shoulders, and settled back into his chair. Grandma regarded us with the patient, resigned expression often reserved for children with wandering
17 minds. "Are we ready?" she asked.

She read the scriptural text for the day, followed by the sermonette written by a Norwegian theologian. The renowned man's arguments battered and retreated, expounded and pleaded. Where was Aunt Gudrun now? I dreaded going upstairs alone to my lonely and chilled bed under the eaves above the kitchen. Grandma's upturned glance met mine. I folded my restless hands upon my lap. Finally she finished reading and turned the pages to the back of the book and read a long, involved evening prayer for the season of Trinity, in which we blessed our friends and enemies, prayed for our government and the President of the United States—and, horror of horrors, for the safety of the King of Norway! This, I felt sure, constituted a mild form of family treason. Then Grandma bowed her head in prayer and placed the welfare of the household into the hands of God, with Whom she lived on understanding terms.

After a nod from Grandma I said good night, climbed the dark stairway, and undressed quickly in the chilly room. I slid between icy, waiting sheets and curled into a small still ball. The light from the register above the kitchen range block-patterned the sloping wall.

Grandpa's voice rose above the howling wind. "Predestination is clearly a fallacy," I heard him say. In the window, dimly lighted by the floor register, I could see the delicate tracery of frost. The old frame house creaked and groaned in the ever rising wind. Downstairs in the room below Grandpa was reading a new theology book: Grandpa was making *his* peace with God.

2

Aunt Gudrun   In our little two-story frame house on the west end of Grand Prairie, North Dakota, there were usually four of us: my grandparents, my red-haired Aunt Gudrun, and I. On week ends, when he smelled a special meal cooking or the delights of bachelorhood grew monotonous, Uncle Sven drove over from a nearby town.

I often worried because Uncle Sven never got married; and I worried constantly that Aunt Gudrun *might* get married. In fact I often lay awake at night, worrying over Aunt Gudrun's unpredictable antics and the flourishing state of her correspondence, mostly masculine. In addition to Aunt Gudrun's job in the county courthouse, where she was a deputy clerk of court, she was also secretary of the local Red Cross. During World War I she supervised the packaging of many oversea bundles. No thank-you letter from a grateful doughboy ever went unanswered, and some correspondence was carried beyond the customary line of duty.

Letters were but a passive threat, and did not warm my fears as they warmed Aunt Gudrun's spirit. But several men of assorted sizes and qualifications menaced my security. While our house had four bedrooms, I had been moved in with Aunt Gudrun as her official bed warmer, and I was never in any mood to brook competition.

Perhaps the most persistent threat came from the ministry. To understand that, you would have to be a Lutheran, and even better a German Lutheran, who un-

19

derstands all the implications inherent in the words "Herr Pastor." But even the Norwegians were bad enough. The minister was almost universally believed in small Lutheran communities to be the vessel of all knowledge, secular and religious.

The problems inherent in the sale of a farm, the courtship of one's oldest daughter, the flirtatious smile of a wife —all could be brought to the door of the parsonage (and probably to the ear of the minister's wife, changing diapers in the next room).

If the clergyman were a bachelor, his importance grew rather than diminished. After the installation and the welcoming handshake were over, the scheming usually started. Old man Anderson on the north forty down by the river had a comely lass Birgit who might be supposed to possess all the qualifications to make the minister happy, despite a set of large protruding teeth and the unpleasant habit of spitting through them when she talked. Mrs. Torkelson, in the big white house on the main highway, had a dear child of thirty-one slowly driving her mother crazy with her brains. Mrs. Torkelson, who had achieved the big house and the silent, glum Mr. Torkelson by a talent for aimless, happy, and incessant chatter, was slowly going mad living in the same house with a mouse of a daughter who had to have a reason for doing things. What better service could Mrs. Torkelson perform for the entire parish than give up Torkla to the new pastor? So while the ladies of the church perspired in the church basement, loading piles of waiting food on the trestle tables and pouring gallons of steaming, aromatic coffee into cups stacked almost to the ceiling, the undercurrent was frequently competitive, if not almost primitively jealous.

Sometimes it was the minister himself who was on the prowl, so to speak. Grandpa, who fancied himself an amateur theologian, was never of any help to my peace; for he encouraged a steady stream of theological if not saintly visitors. One persistent, bald-headed gentleman was a thorn in my flesh, although no particular threat so far as Aunt Gudrun was concerned, as she met any announcement of his arrival with an airy toss of her head and an expressive "Oh, pooh—him!"

I felt the same way; for he walked into a room like a cask of wine being rolled into a cellar. In the old-fashioned manner, even then disappearing, he wore his collar backward. His optimistic moonface, pierced by two raisinlike eyes above a blunt inquisitive nose, usually appeared around the pantry door as I was helping Grandma wash up the dishes of one of his free lunches. "Oh, there you are!" he cried coyly. "And no kiss yet, either." He shook a plump, baby-white finger at me. "When do we get that kiss? Now?" He propelled himself toward me, his girth endangering stacked cups and the washed glassware as he pursued me slowly down the narrow pantry. By this time I was almost prepared to crawl into the dishwater to escape his damp peck upon my cheek. Grandma, torn between helping me out of my dilemma and a Godlike devotion to the clergy, stood wiping her hands upon her apron and murmuring politely under her breath. Usually the old man's persistence and Grandma's obsequious politeness to the cloth cost me a kiss. It seemed most appropriate to me that his name, translated from the Norwegian, meant

"Waterfall." If old Waterfall weren't about, we were likely to be entertaining some itinerant clergyman asked after services to eat some (and often most) of Aunt Gudrun's crusty fried chicken, taste her shimmering perfection salad, and enjoy her fluffy, tart lemon pie.

Yet the clergy never worried my grandparents as a potential source of matrimony for Aunt Gudrun. It was a romance in Aunt Gudrun's past that menaced their peace and security. A decade before, when Aunt Gudrun had been keeping house for a brother in Arizona, she had fallen in love. The classic triangle had developed, with Larry marrying the designing newcomer, and Aunt Gudrun left to remember an unreturned love—with the added handicap of remembering it as it had blossomed and flourished in the romantic and colorful setting of old Tucson.

Larry was free again, freed by divorce, and free to remember Aunt Gudrun as the girl he had really loved and lost in foolish passion. So the letters began, and the advent of every letter left Grandma looking sad and disillusioned, Grandpa huffy. The Church not only frowned upon divorce, it openly attacked it in theory and practice; and in its theology no divorced person ever escaped the taint. These two gentle old people had brought into the world a fiery-haired daughter who gave them kindness and devotion but would not sacrifice her convictions to purchase family peace. "Someday he's coming here," Aunt Gudrun often remarked.

In the meantime Aunt Gudrun had to be content with such as Mr. Piffler, lawyer and local ladies' man. The learned Mr. Piffler had a clammy handshake, accompanied 22 by a soullike searching of the ego behind the hands he was shaking, and a swaying crablike gait that would have served him well when he was shoveling snow. Usually I did not worry about Mr. Piffler, for Aunt Gudrun laughed about him much too heartily and often ever to be serious. He possessed one more redeeming feature: he didn't like a woman; he liked women. His taste ran the gamut from schoolteachers to the clerks in local stores. Also he was handy when you wanted someone to walk home with in the dark. However, he had one passion: picnics, excursions, and trips to nearby towns, which wasn't good, for anything could happen out on the open prairies, even as it can in apartments, canyons, or on mountaintops.

Among Aunt Gudrun's real friends (those she never laughed at) was Grand Prairie's leading doctor, a gruff, blunt, amazingly kind young man. The times Aunt Gudrun sneaked away to dance, she was likely to be with Dr. Whitaker.

One evening when Aunt Gudrun developed a sudden heart flutter, which she was certain heralded her demise, Dr. Whitaker was summoned to the house. This was rather a complicated feat, since we had no telephone, and Grandpa had to dress warmly, hasten across the frozen garden and cornfield to my Uncle Thorvald's house a block away. When the stocky doctor arrived, exuding self-assurance, ether, and gruff good nature, Aunt Gudrun, her long braids tossed gracefully across the hand-embroidered pillowcase, lay there looking pale and sweetly brave.

"What's up, Gudrun?" asked the doctor, making warm clucking noises as he pulled out his stethoscope from a wrinkled black bag. Aunt Gudrun's large and violet-shaded eyes gave him a trusting glance.

"It's my heart," said Aunt Gudrun, trying to rise a little from the pillow.

"Now, we know there's nothing wrong with your heart. Nothing at all . . . well, well." Dr. Whitaker pulled out a bottle of capsules from his jumbled bag, asked for a glass of water from the white china pitcher on the commode. "Here, Gudrun," he comforted, "take this, and try to do the work of one horse, for a change, instead of three." Aunt Gudrun swallowed the pill. Dr. Whitaker snapped shut the lock on his bag, drew up a chair, and then took Aunt Gudrun's hand in his, patting it lovingly.

In the corner by the commode, unloved and unwatched, I stared at them for a minute, and then I dashed into Grandma's room. She was by now occupied in picking up scattered clothes from the floor and placing the comb and brush set on the dresser at perfect right angles to the front, occupations often indulged in when a doctor calls, and probably completely wasted on the medical profession. I threw my arms about Grandma's hips, buried my pigtailed head in the folds of her skirt, and began to sob violently.

"There, there," she comforted. "Gudrun will be all right. The attack has passed." I pulled away and looked Grandma in the face. How could adults be so stupid? It wasn't Aunt Gudrun's health I was now worried about, it was her resistance to the blandishments of Dr. Whitaker.

Dr. Whitaker strode through the door, murmured a few pleasantries to Grandma, and then took the short stairs two at a time. I tiptoed into the room Gudrun and I shared.

The soporific bedside manner of the doctor, coupled with his pill, had worked the desired effect. "Come to bed, Mugs," she invited drowsily. "Come on and help warm this bed. Your half has grown icicles." I turned out the light beside the bed and crawled in beside the sleepy Gudrun. No bed, I mused happily as the moon shone through the ice-encrusted window, would ever be big enough for Aunt Gudrun, Dr. Whitaker, and me.

3

The Sisters   There was one subject upon which my family might be depended to remain silent: my father, past, present, and future. But nothing they might have told me would ever have equaled what I was able to imagine.

For a while I fancied that he might be a criminal granted parole on rare occasions to come and visit us. Tiring of that hypothesis, I wondered whether my grandparents, like Sarah and Abraham, had conceived me in old age and were ashamed of the unusual feat. At other times I imagined that I was the result of some secret union of Aunt Gudrun, perhaps down on the Arizona desert where the moonlight was more potent than elsewhere. Still, it seemed unfair to involve Aunt Gudrun in such an imbroglio, even in my imagination.

Finally I was able to piece out the mystery of my father's continued absence; and while it certainly did not constitute a reasonable excuse for his mild excommunication from our family circle, it appeared to be a sincere one. Aunt Gudrun and Aunt Christina felt that he had been— well, too ardent. In all fairness to them, their conclusion was visibly justified; for when their sister died giving birth to me, she left five children, all under seven.

When my arrival interrupted my brother Carl's toma-hawking on the open prairie, he was only five. After much discussion and some correspondence, he was eventually taken to Tucson, to grow up in an uncle's distant home. The other brother, Alfred, was adopted by a great-aunt in Minnesota, who yearned to fill her childless arms. But her husband apparently looked upon the little red-haired ar-rival as just another mouth to feed, for Uncle Ole (how Norwegians love that name!) loved mammon more than flesh. It was also more pleasant to handle money than a little boy; for you can put money away, in an old syrup pail or under a mattress, but you can't do that to a little boy. He always keeps bobbing up, and is usually wet. When Alfred became a little older, Uncle Ole was able to put him upstairs in an unfinished attic room and keep his money downstairs. Thus on bitter winter nights Uncle Ole was free to count his money, should that be his wont, where no child could disturb him; but the money, in a way of speaking, could.

The three Norns were kinder to the orphaned girls. We were all allowed to remain in Grand Prairie—with frequent side excursions for me to Arizona: my sisters living with Aunt Christina and her husband Uncle Thorvald, and I with my grandparents and Aunt Gudrun. By adoption my pert, copper-haired sister Emily, whom we called Dode, took Uncle Thorvald's name of Rekve. My older sister Bertina was left, like me, with my father's name of Erdahl. When I confronted my gentle grandmother with this legal oversight, she sighed and remarked that in signing away two children (Uncle Ole finally adopted Alfred) my

father had suffered enough. Still, it was Bertina who should have complained most, since she and Dode lived in the same household; but if this difference in legal treatment ever worried her bright spirit, none knew.

In the summer a cornfield and a potato patch, generously covered with red-spotted potato bugs, separated me from my sisters. The potato patch often became a source of welcome revenue, for Grandpa paid Dode and me a penny for every ten bugs we picked. When the financial settlement fell due, we offered to count the potato bugs in front of Grandpa, but Grandpa was a gentleman and settled his account without questioning our veracity. Up at Uncle Thorvald's there was also another source of currency: swatting flies on the sleeping porch, and the rate of exchange was the same.

Every now and then Grandma let me sleep at Uncle Thorvald's. It was with a sense of adventure that I set out across the potato patch, even now stirring with a new generation of potato bugs, past the tall whispering rows of sweet corn to the back gate, where my sister Dode waited for me.

"Are your dishes done?" I advanced, for Grandma's parting advice had made it icy clear where my duty lay should the dishes still be stacked upon my hostess' wooden drainboard. In fact Grandma belonged to the old school which taught that the more self-effacing one was (so long as the principles involved were sound), the more well mannered. Grandma had so well indoctrinated me in this rigorous school of manners that, had not my sister Dode been somewhat similarly reared, I'd never have summoned the courage to wash my hands and brush my teeth in the up27 stairs bathroom. As it was, Dode and I spent the better part of our before-bed ritual suggesting the other one wash first. Bertina, who was now in high school, sailed regally into the dormer-windowed bathroom and settled the delicate matter of protocol by brushing her teeth first. By a vague smile and an expertly raised eyebrow our older sister, whom we had nicknamed Dally, always succeeded in leaving us with the impression that the younger fry were utterly zany.

Downstairs we heard Aunt Christina moving about the kitchen in her steady, sure way. While her steps were always slower than Aunt Gudrun's, they could probably afford to be; for Aunt Tina had caught her man and Aunt Gudrun was still looking. There were other differences, too. Aunt Tina was pretty in a pink and red-gold way; and when she smiled, her blue eyes lit up, with little laughter crinkles at the edges. Aunt Gudrun's face was hardly ever in repose, any more than the rest of her. Aunt Tina, when she spoke to us, meant business; Aunt Gudrun, on the other hand, was always telling us with a laughter-caught voice that she meant business, but she never did.

When we were finally undressed and in bed, we lay awake for hours, keeping up a long whispered conversation that touched upon many subjects but always included: (1) the boys at school; (2) the most recent indignities suffered at the hands of adults; (3) the latest information about how babies were born. This exciting exchange of prejudice and misinformation continued at ever rising crescendo until Uncle Thorvald bellowed in a mock-angry voice, "Aren't you two silly girls asleep yet!"

In the morning I always awakened with the delicious 28 sense that something was different. Beside me Dode lay with her waist-long copper braids flung across the pillow. I sat up in the ornately looped iron bed and looked out the big double upstairs windows, past the cornfield and the potato patch, to our own gray house beside the cluster of gracefully feathered willows in the little hollow. The smoke from the wood stove in Grandma's kitchen curled spirally over the steep-pitched roof and disappeared into the clear prairie air. The Soo Line railroad tracks looked like two silver threads drawn through the greening wheat fields until they disappeared into the clump of trees beside the cemetery.

Faint stirrings in the rooms below announced the family's awakening. I looked apprehensively at my sister Dode, whose long slender arms were stretched indolently above her head. The hall door below burst open.

"Aren't you two lazy good-for-nothings up yet?" thundered Uncle. My feet hit the floor. Dode's green-gray eyes regarded me with wicked amusement.

"Get up, Dode," I whispered.

"He's just teasing."

The hall door swung open again. "If you girls don't get up this minute, I'm coming up to pull you out feet first!" I whisked my black sateen bloomers off the back of a chair. Dode thrust an experimental foot from under the quilts and studied her slender ankle with undisguised approval.

Now came the terrible part of visiting. Was I supposed to remain for breakfast or hit it across the field for home? Of course I knew I was really supposed to stay; but if someone didn't mention me and breakfast in the same sentence, I shouldn't honestly know how they *felt* about my staying. Sometimes at this stage of uncertainty I didn't even want breakfast.

When Dode skipped down the varnished stairway, I followed, nightgown and toothbrush tucked under my arm. In the kitchen Aunt Tina was turning slices of crisping bacon, the percolator chortling and bubbling on a back burner.

"Set the table," she said without glancing up. "Good morning, Mugs. How are you?" She turned toward me for a moment. "Did you sleep well?" she inquired politely.

"Yes, thank you, and thank you for letting me sleep here," I recited.

If I started to help Dode with the plates and cups and saucers, I was surely indicating that I expected to stay; and if I stood there hugging my nightgown and toothbrush, I should also be violating one of Grandma's firmest dicta: always make yourself useful. "Thanks again," I heard myself say, "and good-by." I turned to the rear hallway.

Aunt Tina set down the bacon platter and regarded me with surprise. "Aren't you staying? Don't you want any breakfast?" she asked.

Dode flew through the door from the dining room. "Why, Mugs! I've already set a place for you. Of course you're staying!" she cried.

Aunt Tina suggested, "Go see if your Uncle Thorvald is ready for breakfast." I tiptoed through the dining room, over the blue-carpeted living room, past Uncle's big chair in the corner by the glass-leaded bookcases, past the picture of Sappho with her lyre. Near the dark player piano, with its small, surprisingly classic lines, on which Dode
30   and I often spent ecstatic hours pumping out "The Herd

Girl's Dream" and "The Hungarian Rhapsody, No. 5," I paused to peek around the door into Uncle's bedroom. Uncle, clean-shaven and neat, was putting on his tie in front of the corner mirror above the washbasin.

"How's my bashful little girl this morning?" he asked, giving me a broad smile and a good-natured wink. His deep-set blue eyes, under heavy black eyebrows, regarded me with tolerant amusement.

"Auntie wants to know, are you ready?" I asked.

"Ready for what?" he teased. "Ready for a kiss?" he asked, making a thrust for me.

I fled swiftly through the living room and almost collided with my gray-eyed sister Dally coming from the kitchen with a bouquet of fresh sweet peas for the breakfast table. She set down the vase upon the round dining-room table and put her arm around my neck.

"I'll just bet a certain nice man I know threatened to kiss some little girl around here," she said affectionately.

4

The Coffee Train   Several times a day the singing prairie wind was silenced by the shrill blasts of approaching passenger trains. Late in the morning the flyer from Minneapolis thundered past dark red grain elevators and slid to a screeching stop beside the little yellow depot. In the afternoon, a little after four, the eastbound train whistled at the cemetery crossing, sped past wheat fields and pasture lands, and puffed into the little yellow depot. This Grandma called the coffee train.

31   At the imperious whistle of this red-coached passenger,

the people of Grand Prairie, North Dakota, were reminded it was time to pause for afternoon coffee. A hundred coffeepots were taken from the backs of stoves and placed upon front burners. All over town coffee was served: coffee on oilcloth-covered tables in old-fashioned kitchens like Grandma's with a pump at the sink and an omniscient almanac upon the wall; coffee at lace-draped tables, where Seth Thomas clocks chimed four times from their perches upon golden-oak buffets; coffee served by rosy-cheeked country girls in local cafés; and coffee carried in tin pails by active, exploring hands and often spilled before it reached men waiting in fields.

Home from school, we children smelled the rich aroma of coffee in the air, found plates of sweets and fancy breads upon the table; and sometimes we were included among the adults invited to a coffee party or making an afternoon call. Such an event wore a special luster if it took place some distance from home. Several times during the summer Uncle Thorvald drove his Buick to the Rekve North Farm. When his business had been transacted there, we often stopped to call on the nearby Sturvesons. While Uncle went out to visit with the men in the barn or fields, Mrs. Sturveson invited us into one of her parlors in the big white farmhouse. She exclaimed generously over how we children had grown, complimented Aunt Tina on her appearance, and mentioned how lovely it was that Grandma Henrickson had been able to come along too.

"She's his second wife," whispered Dode.

"Oh," I whispered back, studying my portly, attractive hostess from behind a potted fern on the library table.

"He buried his first wife," confided Dode, dispelling

with cruel abruptness all my bigamous imaginings of a first wife imprisoned on the upper floor.

Grandma, Aunt Tina, and our corpulent hostess threw their very hearts into the adult pastime of birthing babies, marrying off young folk, and burying the old. Finally, when they had become almost surfeited with the exchange of news, our hostess rose and suggested that it was time to have refreshments.

With our hair pulled back in tight braids, our faces scrubbed to baking-pan shininess, we sat upon the stiffest chairs in the hostess' living room and watched our elders play their foolish little game of hide-and-seek with a coffeepot.

"Oh no, we didn't come for coffee!" remonstrated Aunt Tina.

"Don't go to any trouble," echoed Grandma.

But the hostess, halfway up from her chair, wore a smile of purest sweetness. "It just wouldn't be afternoon without some coffee," she said. And we children, who only a week ago had heard her plead in Aunt Tina's living room not to bother making coffee, that it wasn't necessary at all, indeed it was an imposition, enjoyed an amused speculation about the adult conscience.

Finally moving toward the business end of her house, she explained that she would be gone for only a minute, and would we please make ourselves comfortable. Aunt Tina settled back with the pleased air of those who depend upon the familiar to make them happy; and Grandma, her hands folded in her lap, sat with the serene, happy air of those who do not need to possess beauty to enjoy it. We 33 wiggled and slid around on the chairs, ogling at the pictures on the wall and pointing impolitely at a bonbon dish under the library table, where the slanting sunlight revealed a fine layer of dust on each undisturbed piece. Grandma's sober little shake of the head silenced us as the hostess scurried in from the kitchen and placed a plate of chocolate cake upon the table. We watched her take hand-painted coffee cups from the buffet and set them at each plate. Grandma was torn between the desire to offer me as a temporary waitress and the sure knowledge of what I was able to do to a china cup.

"Don't go to a lot of trouble now," called Aunt Tina coyly, looking up from her tatting.

The hostess stood in the dining-room doorway, like a sea gull perched for flight. "I couldn't if I wanted to!" she exclaimed. "You're just going to have to take what I have." By now the palate-provoking aroma of rich coffee pervaded the room; and at every arm-laden entrance our hostess spoke eloquently of her close association with pantry and oven.

At last she stood in the doorway, a fine mist of perspiration on her upper lip and a smudge of powdered sugar drawn across a cheek. "Let's have a sip of coffee," she invited. "But you'll have to excuse me, you caught me at a sort of low point in the pantry."

Grandma and Aunt Tina allowed themselves to be pushed toward the table; and we children followed with the uneager eagerness reproaches and cautioning glances had taught us to assume.

Rich chocolate cake under a heavy thatch of creamy white icing winked insolently at our taste buds. Doughnuts, dipped in a bath of powdered sugar, smelled faintly of nutmeg and lard. Cookies—cookies dropped in fancy shapes from a press, cookies rolled on a board, sliced cold from an icebox and baked, or dropped from a teaspoon— invited in assorted shapes and sizes. The eager hostess thrust a bowl of rich fruit salad mixed with heavy country cream into our busy hands. We sat nibbling at the very edge of the feast lest we be scolded for gluttony and reminded in their frequently mentioned phrase to "behave ourselves."

The afternoon wore on, and the sip of coffee became a long one. Aunt Tina and Grandma made their farewells; and when the hostess later called on Grandma and Aunt Tina she would be greeted with *"Tak for sidst"*—literally, "Thanks for the last time we were together." Thus the Norwegian hostess might swim twice in a sea of gratitude.

But afternoon calls were not always like that. At politely spaced intervals Dode and I were allowed to make an afternoon call upon the childless Rogbys, who seemed to welcome an occasional invasion. They lived across from Aunt Tina's in a two-story, prim box-shaped house surrounded by a strong iron fence.

From the moment we stood upon the front porch taking turns at ringing the doorbell, we were fired with excitement. If old Mr. Rogby, carrying the inevitable newspaper, came to the door first, he stared at us sternly from penetrating blue eyes. We returned the stare bravely, conscious of a betraying twitch under his sharp-pointed gray mustache.

If Mrs. Rogby came to the door, we always heard her heavy slow tread on the uncarpeted hall floor; then her
35 stiff rheumatic hands fumbled with the shiny lock, and

soon she stood staring down at us through her bifocal lenses. "Sven," she called. "Sven, the girls are here." She swung the door open. "Come in, come in," she invited.

Mr. Rogby, the newspaper rolled in his hand, bowed to us with exaggerated politeness and suggested that we women might get along better without his presence, retiring to his heaven, a little portion of the back cellar stairway where the fastidious Mrs. Rogby allowed him to pollute the air with pipe smoke.

She led us across a cold, highly varnished hall, which was always host to the same unaired, sterile odor. To the right rose a curved stairway, its virgin wood practically untrod. What lay beyond the stairs I never knew, though sometimes at night I would lie and imagine the Rogby upstairs peopled with children. My dreams would have been disconcerting to the elderly Rogbys, who achieved a life of most enviable order without them.

We took seats upon the slippery black leather sofa, never entertaining the thought of occupying their large rockers, which sat side by side under the front window. For this visit Dode and I carried little raffia sewing bags, and with great dispatch we drew out our embroidery. Dode's graceful fingers were soon placing neat, ladylike stitches upon a snow-white square of linen. I hoped that Mrs. Rogby's opening remarks would play guard to my fumbling attempts to draw forth my own embroidery, which, as always, lay in a labyrinthine tangle. Finally the Minotaur thrust of an oversized needle warned me that I had found the center of the maze; and I drew out a grayish patch of linen and began to sew on it big, disdainful patches of color.

36

"And how are the family, girls? Grandpa? Grandma? Aunt Tina?" inquired our hostess politely. We assured her they were all well, though the question had seemed superfluous, since Mrs. Rogby, with nothing better to do, had probably watched them all walk in and out of the gate across the street several times that morning.

"Did you read about that violent storm in South Dakota yesterday?" she asked, rocking back and forth and clucking behind her false teeth with the sound of a disturbed hen. "How God," she continued, "if He is good, can allow people to have their homes destroyed by tornadoes, their crops flattened in the fields——" The old woman looked off into space as she clenched and unclenched her large-knuckled hands.

We murmured sympathetically, though a little shocked and even more fascinated by her iconoclastic views, since we had been indoctrinated in the strong, unyielding tenets of Lutheranism.

"When I was a young woman in La Crosse, I was amazed at the things that go on in cities: murders, acts of violence, swindles, human cruelties of every sort. Is God good then? Yes, might I ask, is there a God!" she challenged in a fiery burst of rhetoric. By now she seemed unaware that we were there. "And so many, many wicked people go to church," she said sadly. "And some of the worst occupy the highest places."

"Yes, it is full of sinners," I agreed, wondering wickedly whether my probing grandmother would later extract this heretical admission from me.

"And men, my girls," continued our rocking hostess, "men can be very devils." Her eyes narrowed in thought.

"Only last week I read in my La Crosse paper about a rape." Suddenly she looked over at our scrubbed and shining little-girl faces. "Well, never mind about that now," she finished lamely. When Mrs. Rogby's revolt against Providence was over, and suffering mankind had for the moment been vindicated, she rocked in comparative contentment. On the dining-room buffet through the archway, the hands of her ornate clock pointed to a little after four. From the prairies to the west burst the whistle of the afternoon train. Mrs. Rogby braced her rheumatic frame by pushing her hands firmly on the arms of the cherry rocker, rose stiffly, and started across the slippery hardwood floor.

"You girls must have some refreshments," she said. "No, no, I need no help," she remonstrated as we rose, "but why don't you look at my photograph albums?"

When the swinging door into her kitchen closed upon her, Dode dived under the library table and came staggering up with two heavy velvet-covered tomes. "Which one do you want, Mugs?"

"The red one," I said. We lay down upon the cool floor and began to turn the heavy, cardboard-reinforced pages, peopled with faces we knew almost as well as those in our own family, since we went through this ritual every time we called. Confronted by the typical album pose of the nineteenth century—the hair parted in the center, curling lascivious-looking mustaches, eyes bulging as though a tightening rope were concealed under stiff collars—we were scarcely able to control our rising giggles.

"Aunt Gudrun said years ago Mrs. Rogby used to put
38 a cylinder on the Edison and dance the schottische and

polka for her," I whispered. Our eyes strayed to the phonograph on the library table, from which rose a fluted black horn entwined with pink and blue morning glories.

"Sssh," warned Dode. "Here she comes." Our hostess placed a dainty lace-trimmed lunch cloth upon the dining-room table, took out hand-painted china from the cupboards of the buffet.

"Are you girls happy?" she asked.

"Oh yes," we chorused in gross understatement.

"I'd like to help you," offered Dode politely.

"Oh no!" protested Mrs. Rogby. "You girls are company. Anyway, it's ready."

We sat down to a menu that consisted unvaryingly from visit to visit of hot chocolate, Jello, doughnuts, marshmallows, and cake. Mrs. Rogby, we remembered, was violently opposed to eating commercial ice cream, having frequently regaled us with a long and sad tale of an ice cream poisoning in La Crosse, Wisconsin. The doughnuts, though they had a spicy, elusive flavor, were always a little stale; the marshmallows, in the hands of a mischievous little boy, might have been able to shatter a plate-glass window; and the cake suggested a long acquaintance with a storage container. Still, it was all good and most remarkably satisfying. The Rogbys, we knew, had little company, and even less to do, for they were retired farmers.

Five o'clock came, and with it the family's parting ultimatum that we must leave. Mrs. Rogby waved aside all offers to help with the dishes. "I have little enough to do these days, girls," she protested. We returned the albums to their place under the library table, and Dode folded
39 her embroidery and put it back into her blue-lined raffia

bag. With ill-concealed haste I thrust my sewing away, hoping to avoid the usual adult inquiry as to what I had accomplished and the invariable remark, "Let's see your stitches."

But Mrs. Rogby did not belong to that female clan. We really understood each other well. There were things far more important than filling a waiting square with stitches, when all the world called for a good deal of rocking and thinking.

"We've had a wonderful time, and thank you," we chimed as we stood on the little front porch.

"Come often, girls," Mrs. Rogby invited.

"Grandma won't let me come too much," I explained, but was instantly subdued by a warning glance from my sister.

5

The Rekve Store   Grand Prairie was bounded on the north by wheat, bounded on the south by wheat; the sun rose on wheat, the sun set on wheat, and over it all, by the grace of God, blew the prevailing northwest wind. Almost anywhere you stood, in the little town of Grand Prairie, you could look up a street or down a street and see a field of grain in the distance, or in winter the rough-humped snow burying black loam waiting for the spring plow.

In the Conway Hotel on the corner of Main Street heavy-jowled bachelors so used to freedom they forgot to cherish it, or widowers with wives long ago buried in a plot close to a field of wheat, sat in heavy leather chairs, their feet kicked up against the low window sill, and speculated about the coming crop or talked endlessly of when times had been better, punctuating their slow remarks with a loud clop at a nearby spittoon.

Ranged about the little town stood houses whose every timber and all their furnishings had been wrested from a wheat field. Out of these houses, stooped old farmers, now retired, walked to the post office every day because there was really nowhere else to go. There they patiently dialed their way to an occasional letter and a newspaper or perhaps only to a thin gathering of dust.

Postponing their return home, they stood on street corners or under the shelter of a store front and talked with each other in slow, patient, whining voices about the future of the country and the decline of good government, shuffled home to their aging wives, who fought dust and an occasional predatory child or a disliked neighbor to avert the complete vacuity of boredom.

School children, going home at four, trudged past the depot, hoping the four o'clock train would be late, so that for a moment they might catch a glimpse of life passing by behind a thundering, clanking locomotive. When the afternoon train was late, the children stood waving with hopeful timidity at people behind the dusty, double-paned windows, who returned their stares with curiosity, boredom, or indifference. When the mailbags had been thrown on the red baggage car and the train had exchanged a handful of passengers for a new handful, the locomotive hissed, bumped forward, and chugged with gathering speed past the elevators almost bursting with the wheat of the land. The children watched the disappearing train for a moment, lost in private dreams of wonder, and then

raced homeward across the tracks.

The women of Grand Prairie, meeting at the Rekve Store or the butcher shop on the other side of the tracks, exchanged the news of the day according to the nature of their minds. Among some groups, sagging with bundles and packages, the population of Grand Prairie almost doubled overnight, the number of reputed pregnancies ran so high. Others—with more probity and less curiosity—kept their minds out of neighbors' bedrooms and talked of the weather and social groups, of their small hopes and their little disappointments. At the fringe of every group restless children shuffled feet and ran exploring hands on window sills covered with dust and dead flies, eager to join in play on vacant lots and on elm- and cottonwood-bordered streets.

In the Rekve Store, on a corner opposite the Conway Hotel, whirring cages of money spun high above the counters, up to the little office on a dais near the center of the store. It was money from grimy-handed little boys sent on last-minute errands, money from a farmer east of Grand Prairie in the German settlement, money from a bent little woman whose unmarried daughter had left her a child to rear.

In the high little office, where he could watch the store, sat Grandpa Rekve, bold blue eyes and a straight blunt nose above a curling dark mustache. He looked forward eagerly to Saturday night; for though Grand Prairie seemed to slumber under the high summer sun and pull a heavy cloak of silence about itself during deep winter snows, it always came alive on Saturday nights. Upstairs above the store, Grandma Rekve, dark-eyed, thin, and quick of step, prepared the evening meal in her spotless apartment kitchen and perhaps dreamed of the sod hut on the prairie where she had reared her children and once shooed off a visiting band of Sioux after feeding them a hearty breakfast of wheatcakes and syrup. It was a far cry from their early beginnings, this comfortable apartment in the big brick store building.

In the kitchen in Grandma's house I was hurrying through the evening's dishes so that I might join Dode on the windy corner under the street light and spend Saturday evening in the Rekve Store.

Upstairs Aunt Gudrun was primping for an evening of visiting, when she shook hands with farmers and their wives and enjoyed a cup of coffee in a friendly house after shopping hours were over. "You are not to wait around for Aunt Gudrun," admonished Grandma, "but when the clock in the store points to nine, you come home. Do you want Grandpa to come after you?"

"Dode and I'll walk home together to the corner. I can run the rest of the way," I said, silverware flowing from my hands into an open drawer like pelting hail.

When my sister and I entered the back door of the store a while later, we looked about the busy place with pleasure. All about us the voices of Dakota rose like an off-key chant. There was the deep guttural of German farmers, clustered together in tight little groups; there were the rich, bombastic voices of occasional Russians stressing their words with lordly flourishes; and the sing-song, rapid voices of Scandinavians.

Among them all moved Grandpa Rekve, talking politely in college English to his Yankee customers, exchanging German phrases with a small group hanging on to Old

World customs as tightly as to their purses, greeting the Russians with a hearty handshake and a smile, and sharing genially in the jokes of fellow Scandinavians.

In the hardware store lounged his younger son, Ronald, his feet resting on the counter before him. There the talk ranged from fall hunting to guns and the sloughlike lakes of the Western prairies.

In the dry goods department, or perhaps for a moment in the grocery, the oldest Rekve son, our Uncle Thorvald, waited on customers and nodded and talked and moved about with the restless energy that always characterized his movements. It was he who often saw to it that a pink-striped candy sack went into the grocery box of a family where there were children; or led a family of five to the shoe department to fit the oldest boy with shoes. When the fittings and the talk of crops and inquiries into health were over, five boxes of shoes were likely to go out of the store for Sunday wear.

Among them all stood Ole Swenson, janitor and delivery man, his long face alternately happy or sad, depending upon the thoughts that crossed his mind. His angular frame forever sought a shelf to lean on, a counter to sit on, a doorjamb against which to brace a tired arm. His long jaw underneath a tobacco-stained mustache moved rhythmically with passing thoughts. If anyone spoke to him, Ole felt called upon to rise and smile; and when they had moved on, Ole stroked his graying head, pulled a nondescript cap over his thinning hair, and sat down on the edge of a counter, waiting to carry boxes of groceries to wagons or cars.

The old Rekve Reo, once a family car, had been converted to a delivery truck, and this, the light of Ole's eye, had been put to bed in the alley across from the back of the store. Now all Ole had to live for was Monday morning, when he stacked grocery boxes into the wooden panel of the improvised truck and made his morning rounds about town, knocking gently upon back doors and calling, "Ja. Iss eny-buddy home? Ole Sa-venson and Rekve's Store da-livering gross-cerise. Ja. Iss eny-buddy home?"

In the grocery department black-eyed Mr. Stormann measured coffee and flour, weighed prunes and fruits, and with the deft stroke of a sharp curved knife struck off a bunch of bananas. The strong odor of bar soap and tobacco and barnyard clothes vanished with the grinding in the big red and brass coffee mill, returned, and was vanquished again by gusts of strong night wind that blew in with every customer at the back door.

The freight elevator in the back room thundered to a noisy stop, and Ole, with his aimless, loose, unhurried gait, wandered in to see whether another clerk had thought up a new excuse to keep him busy.

Dark-jawed farmers, leaning against counters and shelves, talked earnestly of politics and land and crops and weather, keeping a wary eye on the womenfolk studying long penciled orders, silenced restless children with a glance of reproof, lighted pipes and cigars or chewed slowly on Copenhagen snuff.

Outside, horses hitched on the south side of the store whinnied and stamped restlessly. Cars driven with the absent-minded abandon of country folk not used to giving right of way lurched to a stop beside the curbing, rattled 45 a moment, and expired in a shuddering cough. Children,

women, and old folk spilled from the doors. High school boys, gathered under a street light, talked in short rumbling bursts while they watched the approach of a cluster of girls; and when the girls passed, flamed into a chorus of laughs and low-voiced comments. Mothers, dragging unwilling little children like heavy laundry bundles, walked up and down Main Street bent on innumerable little errands bought from innumerable little pocketbooks, whose contents they had slaved for all week and begged for, an hour ago, a dollar at the time.

Aunt Gudrun whisked through the front door of the Rekve Store. Her long copper braids wound about her head, she nodded to right and left, shook hands, and waved across the store to friends clustered under the office.

"There's Gudrun Henrickson," a farmer's wife said. "She ought to run for office sometime. Everyone in the county seems to know her."

"Yes, she should," agreed the plump, florid woman with a baby in her arms. "I understand she's planning to have a Red Cross tent at the next county fair so we can leave our babies and enjoy ourselves. That'll be a relief!" she exclaimed. Dode and I moved on.

At the end of the nearest counter stood Anna Norquist, one of our Sunday school teachers. Her rosy, smiling face lit with pleasure as she said, "Finish these chocolates for me, will you, girls?" But we accepted the sack with the full knowledge that they had not been intended for Anna in the first place.

When we caught up with Aunt Gudrun she was shaking hands with a pale pencil of a man whose bristling wheat-colored mustache dominated his thin face. Aunt Gudrun put an arm about my shoulders, scowled with mock disgust, and said, "Straighten up and pull the hair out of your eyes. I want you to meet Mr. Thomsa."

Mr. Thomsa's pale glance darted across my face and settled upon a pile of overalls stacked on the counter behind Aunt Gudrun. "This is my niece," explained Aunt Gudrun, beaming at me as though she hoped to brighten Mr. Thomsa's sober life. "His daughter Hildred is coming to work for us next week. Won't that be nice? You won't have so many dishes to do!"

Mr. Thomsa gave us a frightened little glance and darted an explosive hand in Gudrun's direction. She shook it heartily. "We'll see you next week when you bring Hildred in!" she called to his retreating back.

He looked over his shoulder at us. "*Ja, ja,*" he agreed; and then he disappeared behind the overalls.

"He's nice but rather nervous," explained Aunt Gudrun, who never plumbed the surface, if she could help it, to discover the broken parts of a frail human vessel. She waved to a group of local women coming in the front doors. "Run along now," she suggested, "but remember to keep an eye on that clock!"

Toward the back of the store, among the stacks of buckets and milk pails, Dode held out another sack of candy. "Some man," she whispered, "told me to take this and that he liked my red hair and for Mr. Stormann to give me a sack." She laughed gleefully, deep dimples appearing on either cheek. "Guess he didn't know I belong to the store."

6

Hildred   "*Ja vist*, indeed it's sad to grow old," remarked Grandma. "You never know where you put things. You spend hours looking for articles you should never have lost in the first place."

"What are you looking for now, *Bestemor?*" I asked, coming down the stairway dressed in Aunt Gudrun's long dress, two small sofa pillows stuffed into my bosom, one of Aunt Gudrun's hats perched saucily upon my head.

"My glasses!" exclaimed Grandma irritably. She squinted at me. "What do we have here? *For sind og skam!* For sin and shame! What have you put upon your face?"

"Just a little of Aunt Gudrun's rouge. Please let me keep it on a little while, please."

Grandma lowered her voice and looked cautiously up the stair well. "I was afraid of that. When I saw Hildred the first time I was afraid she'd be a bad influence, the way she colors her face." Grandma shook her head. "How times have changed! Why, in Norway only bad women on the streets of Bergen ever used rose color on their faces!"

"Did they, Grandma?" I asked eagerly. "What did they look like? Why were they bad?"

"Someday, when you grow a little older, I shall have to tell you about that too, I suppose," conceded Grandma. "But what in this big world," she continued with asperity, "have I done with my glasses?"

"*Bestemor*," I laughed, "you're wearing them! Both 49 pairs!"

"*Nei vist!*" she protested. "Have I become that forgetful!"

"One pair on your nose and the other resting in your hair," I explained.

"Fetch my bottle of Beef, Iron, and Wine," she ordered. "I must need strength that food is unable to furnish." She took the pair of glasses from her silver hair. "So that's what I've done!" she exclaimed. "Put my reading glasses on my nose and my work glasses in my hair! No wonder the world began to look awry. Well, fetch the medicine bottle anyway."

"You took some this morning before I left for school," I reminded.

"In that case, leave it in the cupboard," she said. "The wine part I mustn't overdo."

"Uncle Sven says he thinks it's the wine in there that makes people buy it."

"Your Uncle Sven takes too light an attitude toward alcohol right now," scolded Grandma, eying me with a cold glance I felt better reserved for Uncle Sven himself, but rarely delivered to the right source.

In the bedroom above the pantry we heard Hildred Thomsa's tripping steps move between clothespress and dresser. "What do you suppose she's doing?" I asked.

"I told her to go upstairs every afternoon and rest for an hour. Anyway, I don't like strangers underfoot every minute of the day, no matter how nice they are." With the right glasses back on her straight little nose, Grandma gave me an appraising glance. "Go wash off that color. Someone could well drop in for coffee. Anyway, it's bad enough seeing Hildred's posy-colored face every time I turn around in my own kitchen."

On the upstairs landing I tapped experimentally upon Hildred's closed door.

"Caw-um in," whined a thin high-pitched voice with a strong Scandinavian inflection.

"Can I watch you?" I asked the back of a straw-colored head bent over a welter of hairnets, pins, bottles, and cosmetic boxes.

"I suppose so," said Hildred dispiritedly, "but sit down on the bed. You make me nervous, standing close." Hildred turned on me a look of mild disgust. Her pale frizzled hair escaped the knot at the back of her head and corkscrewed down upon her bony spine. Above each ear teetered two artificial buns precariously anchored with stabbing hairpins and covered inadequately by a light frizz of strawlike hair. She picked up a slender bottle from the dresser, shook the pink, chalky fluid vigorously with a jerky twist of her thin wrist.

"Is the teakettle on the stove for supper?" she asked.

"Yes, Grandma put it on for coffee time," I replied. "I heard it singing when I came upstairs."

She poured a little pool of pink liquid into the palm of her hand; then she slapped it on her thin face with sharp little taps, her sallow skin disappearing under patches of bright pink.

"Hard to get on even," she said as though talking to herself. "Glad I learned about liquid powder from that man in the drugstore. Stays on through anything. You can forgit about it, once it's on. Do you like it?"

"It's a very pretty color," I said honestly.

"My skin's too pale. That's the truth." By now Hildred 52 had succeeded in covering her face with this wonder mask, extending the color in a bold line down the front of her neck into the collar of her sheer pink blouse, the unpainted sides of her neck rising like pale twin columns.

"Where do you go every night?" I ventured.

"Who wants to know? Your grandma or your Aunt Gudrun?"

"Just me."

"Oh, just walking or calling on a friend working in town. We look in store windows, go to a show when there's a new one." She glanced quickly at me, sitting on the edge of her bed. "It's none of your business. Don't you know that?"

"I just admire you," I said, "and I like to imagine what you're doing nights."

"You can be sweet at times," she admitted generously, "just like the kids at home. But kids!" she exclaimed. "I know 'em like the preacher knows the Book. I ought to. We've got enough of 'em at home. Never did have a thing of my own till I started to work here. Kids pawing over everything. Not a room without one of 'em in." She picked up a bottle of Ben Hur perfume and spilled it generously into her bosom. "You know, I like pretty things. Scarves, perfumes, fur." A shallow sigh escaped her small bosom.

"Well, I giss I better git downstairs and start cookin' you folkses' supper." She stopped with her hand on the door. "You go do what your grandma told you to do. Wash your face and comb your hair. I heard her. And git out of my room. It isn't that I don't trust you; but I don't want you in my room, that's all." Smelling of talc and Ben Hur perfume and a slight trace of sweaty underwear, she stood holding the door open for me. Her small eyes narrowed as I brushed past. "Run along," she intoned in her expressionless, tired voice. "If you hurry you can sit the table for me."

So we got used to Hildred Thomsa and her face of shocking pink under a cap of blond frizzled hair. Sometimes Grandma sighed a little over the new hired girl's cooking. "The meals are flavorless," she said to Aunt Tina over a cup of coffee in Aunt Tina's dining room. "There's some Swede in that girl. I know it; and if there is, she's just *Svensk* enough to do a good job with breads and pastries."

"She comes in the store a lot, Thorvald says, and her father always asks about her when he comes in to trade. Seems eager to know whether she's pleasing you folks." Aunt Tina reached for a sugar cooky.

"Next summer she'll go like all the help," sighed Grandma, "working in a cook car for the threshers at seven dollars a day."

One morning, later in the winter, I sat by the kitchen sink while Grandma rubbed kerosene into my scalp. "We don't get bugs in school these days, *Bestemor!* Dally says we don't. Why do you have to rub that awful stuff into my hair?"

"Some children *do* get lice in their hair," persisted Grandma with that air of quiet finality against which arguments battered in vain. "You don't because I take the precaution to rub kerosene into your hair before every washing."

"What would happen if Uncle Sven dropped cigarette 54 ashes in my hair?" I expostulated.

"He's fifteen miles away," said Grandma, "so I expect you're safe."

"Can't you find my opal ring anywhere?" I asked, on the trail of anything argumentative.

"Oh, it's probably misplaced, as my glasses often are or like my egg money. I can't find that anywhere."

I wriggled away from the kerosene-saturated cotton. "Maybe it fell into the cistern. Why don't you have Grandpa pump out the cistern today?"

"*Store verden!* Our great world! Pump out all that fine rain water to find an old ring! What nonsense you talk!" Grandma handed me my Norwegian reader while the kerosene soaked into my scalp. "Start your Saturday lessons," she prompted; "then you can spend the afternoon playing."

When I came in at four o'clock, to scent out the quality of refreshments, Grandma met me at the kitchen door with her finger on her lips. "Be still!" she admonished. "Sit down to the kitchen table and have some cinnamon rolls. No matter what happens upstairs, you must say nothing at all. It is rude to embarrass anyone, no matter what has happened." I looked at Grandma as though her tongue had parted company with her senses.

I was soon conscious of a low rumble of conversation upstairs, with an occasional high whining like the mewing of a kitten.

"Is Hildred sick?" I whispered.

"Worse than that," answered Grandma, "but be still now."

Down the stairway came a clatter of shoes; and I looked
55 up to see Uncle Thorvald enter the kitchen, followed by

a dejected-looking little man with a face as long as a sour pickle, whom I recognized as Mr. Thomsa, Hildred's father.

Uncle Thorvald's expression was worried and sad. "I am sorry, Mr. Thomsa, that it had to be me to discover this," he remarked at the foot of the stairs as Hildred's father came to the landing.

Mr. Thomsa shrugged his narrow shoulders in a hopeless gesture and fought the tears welling in his mild blue eyes. "We are all sorry," he said, "but I am filled with shame." He turned to Grandma, who stood by her rocker near the kitchen stove, and his tone was a spiritless monotone. "She's packing her things. I'll drive by with the team when I settle with Thorvald, and pick her up."

While Grandma tried to find a suitable reply, the little man slipped out the kitchen door into the chilly back entry. Uncle Thorvald stood at the threshold, hat in hand. "I am sorry, Mor," he apologized, "sorry that you will be left without help." Grandma nodded her understanding; and soon their steps were crunching past the kitchen window on the snow-covered wooden sidewalk.

That evening Grandma talked at some length about Hildred's leaving. "You see," she remarked in the platitudinous way of the Norwegian, "your Catechism I am making you learn isn't only a book. It's a rule of life you may follow. Hildred, poor soul, sinned against the Eighth Commandment."

"Did she steal my opal ring and your egg money too?" I asked.

"We never asked her about that," replied Grandma. 56 "Surely she had enough shame over the dresses she stole."

"It beats me," remarked Aunt Gudrun, embroidering on a pillowcase for her hope chest, "how she ever got out of Rekve's Store with all those stolen dresses!"

"Thorvald says she went into the fitting room, tried on a few dresses, bought and paid for one, and wore out a stolen dress under the old dress she wore into the store."

"Well, she was thin enough to get by with it," remarked Aunt Gudrun. "I feel sorry for her family, though. Mr. Thomsa has the air of a man pitifully eager to please."

I asked, "Why did she do it?" I thought of the dark room at the top of the stairs, with its clinging odor of perfume and cosmetics, and powder and hairpins spilled by her hurried packing and lying scattered upon the floor.

"She couldn't help herself," explained Aunt Gudrun. "She was a kleptomaniac."

"A big word to cover a bigger sin," sighed Grandma.

"No, it's really a disease," explained Aunt Gudrun.

Grandpa looked up from his latest Rölvaag novel. "Well," he said with the slightly arrogant little sniff he saved for women's prattle, "whether it's a disease or not, it left its mark upon her face. I couldn't go out to the pantry after a drink of water without thinking I was running into a prairie fire."

7

The Visitor   For a price we were always welcome in Selma Rekve's back door.

While the open sesame to Aunt Christina's kitchen often appeared to be the willingness with which we picked 57 up a waiting dish towel and made ourselves useful, in her sister-in-law Selma's it often seemed to be the readiness with which we divulged information and answered questions.

One spring day, when the snow had thawed to fill sloughs and when little melting rivulets coursed through black fields waiting for the plow, I was in Selma's kitchen playing with her gentle-mannered daughter Solveig. Selma was busy at the sink. Her eyes frequently strayed from her work to the vacant lot bordering the lane to Grandma's house.

"My goodness!" she exclaimed. "There goes your grandpa! What in the world is he walking to town for now?" Grandpa was passing the big red barn which had once housed the delivery team for the Rekve Store. He crossed his hands behind his back, and his head was bent forward in his usual reflective pose. Selma's dish towel hung soggy and limp over her left arm. "What's he going to town for now?" she reiterated.

I looked up at her provocative, round face, at her merry little mouth under the long upper lip, and at her plump cheeks with their high color. Certainly in Selma there was an active curiosity that clamored for satisfaction. "He's meeting the afternoon train," I improvised glibly.

"Well, I do declare!" she said, dropping her towel upon the sink and placing her hands upon her hips. "Isn't that something different? What's he meeting that train for?"

Grandpa's slow but steady gait was taking him out of range. The shrill whistle of the Coffee Train only served to substantiate my rash statement.

I turned back to the doll clothes Solveig and I were sewing. "Oh, he just has to," I replied vaguely, hoping 58 Selma would drop her profitable inquiry.

But Selma's terrierlike mind pursued its scent. "What for?"

"Well," I began, now so deep in a lie that there seemed no logical escape but to give it a dash and put an end to it, "well, Uncle Henry is coming."

"Good heavens!" she exclaimed, while I studied her furtively to see whether she was regarding this as a game or something to report to Grandma. "Don't tell me!" She picked up a dish and began to wipe it with haste. "You mean your Uncle Henry from Tucson?"

"Yes, way from Tucson," I said, now completely overawed by the number of devious methods by which adults could trap unwary children into a pit of trouble. Solveig, her lovely brown eyes big with wonder, had put down her doll; and Signe, a toddling, two-year-old duplicate of Selma, stood in the dining-room door entranced by a drama she could not understand but seemed to enjoy.

"Why hasn't your grandma or your Aunt Gudrun told us? Why is it a secret?"

"We didn't know about it until today," I extemporized, to my own surprise.

"Think how surprised your grandma must have been! She thinks so much of Henry; he's her oldest son, you know."

Should I attempt to bolt out the back door and admit defeat, or meet my opponent on such unfamiliar ground?

"But tell me," persisted Selma, "why he happens to be coming on the afternoon train when everyone knows people from Tucson usually come by way of Minneapolis, on the morning train."

"Well," I began, searching wildly for an opening in the

thicket of lies in which I was caught, "he decided to see new country on the way up here."

Selma went to the back door and pulled a red sweater off the hook. "Girls," she said, "I'm going over to see your Aunt Tina for a few minutes. Now all of you stay right here and play until I get back. Understand?" She wagged a finger at us and warned us to be good.

"Gosh, Mugs," said Solveig, "things sure happen fast sometimes, don't they?"

"I think I better leave," I said, hating the room and even the children in it for the moment for their being witnesses to my fall from truth.

"But you *can't* go," argued Solveig patiently. "You heard Mother, and we always mind each other's parents."

Selma's kitchen clock ticked on; and across the vacant lot Grandpa ambled down the pathway, reading the front page of the *Skandinaven* as he walked. The frisking wind began to abate, whispering softly of spring twilight and a vernal earth. I itched to get away from the warm kitchen and the chattering girls. Then the back door slammed.

"I think you better go see your grandma," said Selma, pulling off her red sweater. "She's waiting for you in Tina's back yard. You handed me a surprise," she said, "and now I think you've got one coming yourself."

I thrust my arms into my coat, muttered good-by, and ran quickly out of the house.

Across the fence from Selma's yard, I saw Aunt Tina by the clotheslines, standing tall and straight, and beside her, Grandma's smaller figure, wrapped warmly in a long dark coat.

60   "Well, Magrit," said Grandma, "I've been told you

have spent a busy afternoon weaving fairy tales." Aunt Tina, in looking down at me, managed to convey the expression that she had inadvertently stepped upon a grass snake. "Come, we'll go home." At the gate Grandma began to pick her way carefully across the muddy field. When she gained a piece of dry soil she turned and said, "Of course what you need is some soap to wash away the strong coating of untruth which covers your words." Grandma's set, firm glance was tempered by a vast amount of sadness, as though her lifetime of work with children had fallen like an avalanche at her feet. "But," continued Grandma when we had reached our back yard, "there are other things to concern us tonight, for your father is here."

Grandma walked on. I stood still. Monsey cat frolicked across the dry grass and rubbed his black fur against my stockings.

"Come now," said Grandma, "you must change your dress and have your hair combed." Grandma ushered me into the warm kitchen. The door into the front part of the house was closed, and from the other side came the familiar low rumble of my grandfather's voice and a quick, answering cadence that left me trembling inside.

"Is Aunt Gudrun home yet?" I whispered to Grandma.

"Yes, upstairs. Have her clean you up."

In the bedroom above the kitchen Gudrun was combing out her waist-long hair, which fell across her shoulders like molten copper. "Oh, it's you," she said.

"Grandma says please fix me up."

Her comb in mid-air, Gudrun turned away from the mirror and looked at me with an expression entirely strange in her usually pleasant face. "For him?" she asked.

61

"No, thank you." She laughed sarcastically. "I wouldn't fix up either you or myself."

Down in the kitchen I heard Grandma setting plates upon the table.

"Why did he come, Aunt Gudrun? Is he going to take me away?" I asked, stroking her silk dress and savoring her nearness.

"Well, I don't care!" she exclaimed. "He better not try to. Who does he think he is, barging in unannounced like this?" Gudrun took the long braids she had finished plaiting and wound them around her head.

"You look all right," she said. "You better go down and help your grandma."

"Have you seen him yet?" I ventured.

"I said hello and that's all I intend to do," she replied.

"Won't you even talk to him at supper?"

"I'm not staying for supper," said Aunt Gudrun, applying her powdered rouge with little whisks of the puff. "I'll be up at Christina's."

"Magrit!" called Grandma, her voice rising through the floor register. "Come down!"

"Will you be sleeping here tonight?" I asked.

"I'm so mad right now I can't tell what I'm going to do." I hesitated in the doorway. It was easy to see there was no comfort to be found in Aunt Gudrun this evening. I tiptoed noiselessly down the stairway.

"Well, *smaagjenta*, my little girl," said Grandma, turning away from the stove, "let's go in and see your father. He has waited long enough."

She opened the door into the living room. "Here she is, Marcus," said Grandma, while my hold on her hand grew tight with desperation. The man beside our library table looked up with a sudden glance from which I seemed unable to turn away, and then he rose to greet me.

"Take his hand," whispered Grandma, nudging me forward. His fingers enclosed my hand in a firm grasp. I jerked away quickly, backing to the safety of Grandpa's knees.

"So this is how the smallest has grown!" he exclaimed, seeking his chair by the library table but his gray-flecked eyes never leaving my face.

"They grow away from us quickly," sighed Grandma.

"These years since—I don't know where they have gone. The pity of it is——" he began.

"I know," sympathized Grandma. "But it is best this way, Marcus. They were too small. What could you have done for them alone?"

"And there has never been anyone else," he said quickly. He studied my face. "Would you be so kind as to sit on my lap?" he asked.

"No, thanks, I like *Bestefar's* best," I said, climbing with alacrity to Grandpa's knees. A shadow of sadness drifted across his lean face, and his eyes seemed to darken. He picked up something from the library table.

"I have started a bankbook for you," he said. "Something your own, and not what I send to your grandpa for you." I made no reply. "Won't you come over here and get it?" he asked.

"No," I said, "you can just hand it to *Bestefar* sometime. Thank you anyway." My words came to my own ears as from a great distance. "I don't really want it."

63   "Magrit!" cracked Grandma's shocked voice from the

doorway. "Marcus, forgive her," she apologized. "She can't have any idea how she sounds——"

"I know," my father said, fingering his vest front nervously. "I come as a stranger to all my children."

Grandma turned on me a look of sharp reproof as she nudged me toward the kitchen. When we were in, she closed the door between us and the two men who sat, silent, in the living room.

"I have never been so ashamed in all my life!" she exclaimed. "*Skam!*" she scolded. "Shame! How can you talk so unfeelingly to anyone, let alone your own father?"

"*Bestefar* is really my father," I said, beginning to sob, "because *Bestefar* feels like my father."

"Well," said Grandma, going to the stove to stir a bubbling pot, "this was not all started in one day, so I think the answer to all this cannot be found in a day. Go wipe your eyes and make yourself presentable. You might have known," she continued, "that when you told such fantastic lies up at Selma's this afternoon your day would come to a bad end."

"Do I have to eat supper?" I asked.

"Not if you are unable. But no matter how mixed up you feel," she said, "you are commanded to honor parents. It's as simple as that," said Grandma, dishing up dinner and settling the matter of filial duty at the same time.

Upstairs I undressed and drew the latch across the door. I did not fall asleep until I heard my father leave for Aunt Tina's. When I drew the bolt back on the bedroom door for Aunt Gudrun's coming, I felt the Lord was taking an active and rather uncomfortable hand in my affairs. How 64 else could my father's arrival have been timed with such exquisite nemesis upon the hour of my flight from truth?

8

The Homestead   Grandpa decided the time was ripe to return for a summer's visit to the old claim, where he and Grandma had homesteaded in western North Dakota years before. It lay in a stretch of Dakota prairie where the wind sang all summer, uninterrupted by the sound of automobiles, where coyotes prowled at night, slinking through the long prairie grass. "We'll take the girls along for company," said Grandma.

So one day Uncle's Buick left Grandpa, Grandma, Dode, and me in the lonely little farmhouse on a rise overlooking a fenced pasture, a field planted to wheat, and miles of grassland with swelling hills and deep gullies.

The house, only rarely occupied by hopeful renters, had the dispossessed air of a place left alone to the onsloughts of winter, to the monotonous rains of early fall, and to the dry glaring heat of a Western prairie summer. So left to itself, it developed an anti-social character, its old timbers creaking with tales of the past, like an old crone muttering away her loneliness. The tar paper on windy nights slapped irritably at the aging boards upon which it lay; and the mice and rats in the cellar below made experimental journeys between the rotten studdings. The three-room frame house sat upon the rolling prairies like an abandoned houseboat upon a lonely lake.

During the day Grandpa puttered about the collapsing old barn, busy with one lonely cow and a sad-looking horse in the sloping pasture below. Grandma cooked the simple dishes of the old upon a stove threatening to collapse even before the little house did. Now and then she would look out the narrow little window and commune with the past, seeming to sense that one can never go back, only lean a bit backward. Dode and I climbed the steep hill beyond the heading wheat field, where the sharp, redolent sage nodded in the wind and the long grass moved with the wind's blowing as though brushed by the hand of God.

"I'll bet the Sioux Indians loved it here," said Dode, pulling a long grass and savoring its strawy, burned-in-the-sun flavor.

From the huge rounded stone on which I sat I saw prairie dogs sit upon their haunches, regarding our encroachment upon their lonely acres with an amiable curiosity. "Maybe an Indian sat on this rock," I said, shuddering at the image my mind conjured up. Below the hill the little frame house rose out of the tall prairie grasses like a wooden box dropped from a wagon, its colors fading into a oneness with the infinite landscape. The deep-rutted wagon road rose and fell with the contours of the hills, disappearing into the air at the crest of the farthest one. A few clouds, like huge melted marshmallows, were splotches of brilliant white in the deep blue bowl of the sky.

"What are we out at the homestead for?" I asked.

Dode studied the scene below us. Then she replied in her gentle voice that always seemed a startling contrast with her fiery hair and boyish freckles, "I don't know, Mugs. Except that Aunt Tina said Grandpa and Grandma 66 get lonesome for this place now and then."

"I don't know if I like it here," I replied, "because it's lonesome here, and nothing ever happens."

But one day, not so much later, Grandpa hitched the old gray horse to an ancient buckboard standing in the barn, and announced that we were going visiting. Grandma, packing sandwiches into an old stone crock, told us to wash up well in the basin standing on the cracked chair by the back door, and then go in and put our Sunday dresses on.

When we looked clean and fresh enough for the day's venture, she loaded the picnic lunch into the front of the carriage and told us we might sit in the buckboard above the wheels. Grandpa gave the tired old horse a smart slap with the loose rein, and we were off, Grandma holding onto her little black sailor hat with tight-clutched hands. She wore her Sunday skirt of fine black wool and a crisp lawn blouse of purest white, down which two panels of open cutwork, known as Hardanger embroidery, ran to the waistline. At the high neck of her blouse she had fastened a gold *sølje*, a heart-shaped Norwegian pin from which three gold disks dangled, tinkling and dancing in the whipping wind.

The horse trotted on the high grassy arc between the ruts of the typical prairie road, the carriage creaked and bounced; and Dode and I sang roundelay after roundelay in our high-pitched girl voices. Grandpa, serene and stately, held the reins in his old veined hands and looked like the chiseled statue of some Viking at the prow of a sharp-nosed boat. The road rose and fell, climbed up, went down, turned sharply to go around a slough sunk deep in
a hollow between two steep hills. Where the water had

receded lay patches of mud, caked and tiled into geometric shapes by the hot summer sun.

On a rise Grandpa brought the horse to a stop, looked to the right and left, and then turned the carriage on a stretch of fine graveled state highway. In the distance we saw a church spire, topped by a large wooden cross. The wind sang in a steady high timbre; the gravel hit smartly against the rolling wheels.

In the meantime Grandma and Grandpa had grown silent, the carriage began to slow down, and the wind sang in soft, sibilant whispers. In the grass-grown church-yard Grandpa drew the carriage to a stop.

"Is this where we are going to picnic?" I asked, leaning over the seat to check upon the safe arrival of the brown stone crock.

"*Nei, det er ikke.* No, it is not," replied Grandpa. "Jump down."

Grandma got slowly down from the high seat, Grandpa holding onto her arm. The two stood there looking at the weather-beaten church; then their glances traveled together toward a cemetery at the rear of the neglected grounds. As their steps whispered through the tall blowing grass, they seemed to have forgotten us.

"Come, girls!" called Grandpa at last, turning to see us standing uncertainly by the carriage. Grandma stood beside an uneven little mound, the knuckles of her folded hands looking white and knotted.

"I thought you would like to see where your mother lies buried," she said quietly. She knelt down and began to pluck weeds off the grave in the aimless way people move 69 when their minds are far away. I looked up at Grandpa, standing tall and straight beside her, his eyes gazing far off into space where the soft rolling hills met the blue sky. Large tears were coursing down his cheeks and falling unheeded to his vest below. Dode's quick little hand sought mine.

When I looked down at Grandma piling weeds in a neat little stack beside her, my glance was drawn to a row of gopher holes tunneling deep into the mound.

"*Nei, nei!* No, no!" I cried, and fled to the waiting carriage and the patient old horse nibbling grass in the churchyard. Dode was behind me, and when I clambered up into the carriage she flung her arms about me. "Don't cry," she said. "Don't cry, Mugs. She's really not there. Don't you know that? Don't you know that?" she asked.

Our grandparents came toward the carriage quickly, their heads bent and their voices silent. But before they climbed in they looked back again to the little unfenced plot beside the aging wooden church.

"It's such a neglected place to leave anyone as young as she was, and as good," said Grandma. Grandpa did not reply, but shook his head as though there were no words to soften such a lonely sight. They climbed in, and Grandpa nudged the horse to a gentle start; and when I dared look back, all I could see was the church with its spire lifting into the bright noon sky.

Farther on, Grandpa turned the buggy off the graveled highway and turned down a grassy road skirting a lake that lay in a hollow made by encircling hills like water in a cupped hand.

"There's a clump of bushes over there," said Grandpa.
70 "Shall we stop there and open our food?"

"I am afraid they will not be too hungry." Grandma spoke with a sigh. "I had no wish to spoil their day, but what else could we have done? I could not leave this land without a call to where she rests."

"Children forget," said Grandpa, stopping the horse beside a clump of poplars and Juneberry bushes. "And we who cannot forget learn to accept the inevitable. Turn them out to pasture or to wade in the lake. They will eat. You'll see."

Grandma had us help her carry crock and parcels to a shady spot above the lonely lake. "Take off your shoes and stockings," she said, "and wade about the shallow edges of the lake." We tucked our dresses into our bloomers and ran up and down the quiet shore. Grandpa had climbed a distant knoll and stood there surveying.

"What's he looking at?" I asked Dode.

"Our parents had a house here once," she said. "The one the lightning struck before they got moved in. Aunt Tina told me once."

Grandma stood upon the little bluff and waved for us to come. We sat down to eat; and while hunger rescued us from the gnawing feeling at the pit of our stomachs, it could not chase all the specters away. Grandma, usually so quiet, prattled on as if light words could frighten shadows.

"Our next stop will be a visit to an old friend," she said. "They have a little girl, and you will like to play with her." We helped her load the remnants of our lunch into the buggy, and soon we were off into the rounded hills again.

Several miles farther the carriage jogged to a stop beside a house and barn hovering under the protecting arm of a
clanking windmill.

"They're home," said Grandma, spying a curtain in the living room move quickly back into place.

"Where else would they be?" asked Grandpa, climbing down from the buggy. "They are farmers. It is only we who have declared this to be a holiday."

Out of the back door stepped a tall, erect woman, her dark hair braided and twined around a well-poised head.

"This is Mrs. Hanson," said Grandma. Mrs. Hanson enfolded us in warm, enthusiastic embraces.

"*My* Ole," she remarked to Grandpa, "you will find in the barn." She turned back to Grandma. "But come in. Come in," she invited in a deep throaty voice. She put her hand upon Grandma's arm. "How welcome you are you surely must know." She ushered us into the house, leading us through a small tidy kitchen into a front room comfortably furnished with waiting rockers and a table covered with a snowy white cloth embroidered in painstaking Hardanger work. An old clock on the wall ticked away the quiet country minutes, and the west wind of the Dakota prairies pushed at the lace curtains in graceful, billowing swells.

"Helga!" called our hostess. "Helga! Come here." Mrs. Hanson glanced at Grandma out of deep-set soulful eyes. "She's a bit shy, I suspect."

The wall telephone buzzed shrilly. "Excuse me, please. I'm Central here," she apologized. She took up the receiver. "Why, sure, Mrs. Yonson, I'll ring them for you." The throaty Norwegian r's rolled off her tongue like breakers on a distant shore. "Do you remember the Henricksons from Grand Prairie?" she asked into the instrument. "*Ja. Ja.* Sure they're the ones. And they are here for coffee. *Ja.* Sure," she intoned. "I'll call you and tell you all about the viss-sit later."

A door at the side of the room opened, and on the threshold paused a girl of eight or nine, barefoot, her heavy dark hair falling in half-plaited braids across her chest. "Come in, Helga," commanded her mother, smiling. "These are the Henrickson—I mean the Erdahl—girls whose mother lies in the churchyard not too far away. You remember, dear?"

Helga took her hand off the doorjamb and slid quickly into a straight chair by the door. When she turned to look at us with a shy little smile, we saw that her other arm hung withered and useless.

"Have you taken a trip to Norway lately?" asked Grandma.

"*Ja*, Helga and I were there only a few years ago." Mrs. Hanson rose. "But we'll talk about that later over our coffee," she said. Grandma began the usual academic protests of the polite Norwegian, but was as quickly silenced by the equally academic replies of the determined hostess. "Helga, take the girls out and show them the kittens and the newborn calf," she suggested. With a shy smile Helga rose and opened the front door for us. I admired the deft way she handled the door and determined once I was back to my grandparents' old claim shack to practice one-handed feats of my own. Outside in the windy yard, Helga led us to the mewing kittens and to the barn to see the wobbly newborn calf. But it was the heavy pounding clank of the windmill I liked, and the wind's work upon the shiny whirring steel blades.

73   When Mrs. Hanson called us in for coffee the kitchen

table was draped with a white linen cloth intricately edged with cut lace. Norwegian silver glistened beside the plates. Grandma remarked how beautiful the table looked. Mrs. Hanson laughed with a throaty chuckle. *"Ja,* it is strange," she said, "but I have always found that humble surroundings seldom prevent a Norwegian woman from having and cherishing some of the finer things for the table. It is so in Norway too." She urged us to the table.

Mr. Hanson, washing at the sink and wearing his stained and wrinkled work clothes, cast his wife a glance that seemed to say he had little taste for interruptions of this sort, much less a table set with women's finery. He settled down to the table at last, his heavy dark mustache twitching nervously above his somber mouth.

When the time came to leave, the sun was close to the fringe of hills we had crossed earlier in the day. Grandpa left the graveled highway and traveled on a lonely prairie road all but overgrown with the summer's grasses. Near by, birds circled lazily over a deep slough filled with weeds and cattails. In the distance a dejected-looking box of a house covered with peeling tar paper stood beside the green wheat field.

"Who lives here, *Bestefar?*" I asked.

"I know," interrupted Dode. "I know all about it. This is Aunt Tina's old claim shack, isn't it, Grandpa?"

"Ja vist, so it is," he replied. He slowed the horse down. "Do you want to get out?"

"What was it for?" I asked, clambering down quickly from the buggy lest Grandpa change his mind.

"Your Aunt Tina lived here alone, even through a
74 stormy winter, to lay claim to this piece of land years ago,"

said Grandma, getting down to join us, her skirt trailing on the overgrown grass beside the hut. "Well," continued Grandma, standing before the boarded door, "she did have Shep, her collie dog, with her to sleep on her feet cold nights and bark away the coyotes." When we had encircled the boarded-up shack again, Grandpa called impatiently from the little carriage.

"Our waiting cow needs to be milked. She has no interest in claim shacks."

We climbed back into the buggy, and I took a backward glance at the lonely shack, standing beside the reedy slough of water. In the blue twilight of that northern land it stood like the deserted dwellings of half-remembered dreams, and I knew I should meet it again and again. I shivered in the cool night air.

Back in the little farmhouse Grandma prepared us a bedtime snack and hustled us off to get our sleep. She carried the coal-oil lamp into the little room and saw us safely into the bed. "Say your prayers," she admonished, blowing out the lamp and joining Grandpa in the kitchen.

Far off in the hills a predatory coyote, primed for a night of hunting, barked sharply. We moved closer together. Between the studdings back of our bed a mouse moved stealthily, then, gathering courage from the quiet house, raced with deft sureness up the black framework of the house.

I seemed to stand once more above a little plot of earth where four-footed animals raced and tunneled. I sat up in bed and screamed.

"Come quickly, *Bestemor!* Come quickly," called Dode, her slender hand upon my arm. "We need you!"

9

Saturday   So far as Grandma was concerned, I was her pigtailed Sisyphus rolling a small stone of knowledge up a Norwegian hill.

It didn't matter that it was Saturday, that newly sculptured snowbanks extended from garage roofs and chicken coops, swirling downward in graceful arcs of hard-packed snow. It didn't matter that all the children in the neighborhood were out on sleds and skis or sliding down miniature hills on icy bottoms. It didn't matter that Grandpa had given me my first pair of skis, sawed and planed and tempered to graceful curves in his cellar workshop. What did matter, to Grandma, was that Saturday was the day I coped with the beginnings of Luther's Catechism and any Norwegian fairy tales she considered suitable for a child's edification.

So I lay upon my stomach in the chilly upstairs bedroom memorizing questions that it seemed silly for Luther to ask if he already knew the answers. Outside the "heathen" children whooped and hollered, challenged and retreated, honorable specimens of the temporal rewards offered by an ungodly life.

Grandma had often tried to temper her week-end assignments with a gentle remark such as, "I am old, Magrit. I must know that I have done my best with you while there still is time. It's a strange thing," she continued, "to contemplate that all you have known and felt and believed might perish with you, unless perhaps you can touch another's mind." She had sat down then in her rocker by the coal range, beside the bread left to rise under its protective blanket of a discarded purple quilt; and for a space she merely rested, her brown-spotted hands idle for a change.

"Won't you remember this earth when you live in heaven?" I asked.

"Who knows? And who would count much of life worth remembering?"

"Do you have a lot to forget, *Bestemor?*" I persisted.

"A lot to forget, a lot to remember." The rocker creaked, and she straightened the folds of her printed alpaca skirt. "I should like to forget the good I might have done and remember what I have not been able to do. That would be humility."

"How old are you, *Bestemor?*"

"As old as the hills of course, *smaagjenta.*"

Monsey cat stroked his sleek black fur against her skirts. "I often tell you about Norway," she continued, "because I have had a love for it that clings beyond the length of memory. To forget one's mother country in a new land is to forget the talking of one's heart. Never be ashamed of that."

"Tell me again about the drowning in the fjord!" I begged.

"That can I do if you will fetch my knitting."

When I came back from upstairs she picked up the gray yarn and her sharp steel knitting needles, studied the ribbing on Grandpa's socks for a space, and began, "It happened when I was a young girl and there had been a wedding in Ullensvang, the church across the fjord from where we lived. My cousin was among the wedding guests.

"After the ceremony the bride and groom and the wedding party stepped into the rowboat to return to the side of the Hardanger Fjord where we lived. It was a fine day, and neither storm nor strong wind to mar a crossing we had often made. Indeed, as I often told you, we always took a boat to church, as folk today would drive a car.

"But these were young people and the bride was lovely in all her Hardanger finery, with silver ornaments and bright-colored embroidery upon the bosom of her dress. But any wedding was an event in our quiet, busy lives." Mons settled on his bed beside the range. The rich essence of yeasty dough began to pervade the room.

"As they were crossing, one of the young men suddenly stood up in the boat, picked up the flintlock gun that lay upon the seat, and fired it with a glad shout so that all might know the wedding was over and the bride and groom returning."

Grandma's knitting needles stopped their clicking, and the brown rocker stood still.

"A spark from the gun hit the powder chest at his feet and the boat exploded. The bride, the groom, my cousin, and all the attendants were blown into the deep water of the fjord, with the wreckage of the rowboat splintered all around them. The bride, dressed in the silver-ornamented headdress and the rich finery of a Hardanger wedding, went down into the deep water and never came up again. The groom, too, perished." Grandma sighed.

"And your cousin?" I asked, knowing well the answer, but having to hear it again.

"My cousin sank into the deep waters twice, but was
78 rescued." Grandma resumed her knitting. "It was an event

almost too sad to contemplate, the loss of so many young people all at one blow, needed out of love or necessity in many sorrowing homes. Your grandpa tells me, but I myself would not know, that Tidemann has painted a famous picture of that fated bridal crossing and Grieg himself wrote the music to a poem commemorating the sad event."

Now upstairs, I lay upon the bed and watched the children skating on the willow slough below the window, the fine snow swirling in dancing swoops across the ice and settling against the banks fringing the little frozen pond. Between the storm window and the inside pane of glass lay a miniature, browning snowbank, mute evidence of the force of the wind on stormy nights.

When lunch was over and Grandma had heard my lessons, she had to leave. "Take your Catechism and your reading to *Bestefar*," she said, "when you have washed up the dishes."

It was almost three o'clock before Grandpa came around and Grandma's return seemed imminent. Grandpa settled down in a big rocker in the living room, close to the west window, where the cold bright sun of a Dakota winter gleamed deceptively summerlike through the double panes behind the frosty lace curtain. Both of us came prepared to this rendezvous, Grandpa with a novel under the *Skandinaven* upon his lap, and I with a fairy tale under the Catechism.

"How did you get that bump on your forehead?" I began.

"Oh, that!" exclaimed *Bestefar*, as though I had not asked the question a hundred times. "Well, that happened in Norway when your grandma hit me with a hammer." His frosty mustache twitched above a little smile, and his blue eyes laughed at me.

"Why?"

"I did not settle down as a proper married man soon enough to please your grandma, who at times can be a little strict."

"Yes, I know," I said. "But tell me in truth, Grandpa."

"So you must have the truth," he said. His mild eyes grew purposely bigger for my edification. "If you must know, I grew a little bump upon my head to hold the extra knowledge I must carry, as one who must live among so many women all his life."

"I think you're probably joking," I said.

His hand reached for my brown Catechism. "And I think you are leading me on beyond the work you have been told to do. Let's see now," he said, opening the little book. "What is your lesson?"

"The Fourth and Fifth Commandments."

He scrutinized the book through the lower part of his glasses. "All right, go ahead," he prompted.

"But Grandma doesn't do it like that. She asks the questions."

"All right, all right," said Grandpa. "What is the Fifth Commandment?"

"Honor thy father and thy mother that it may be well with thee and thou mayest live long upon the earth."

The room was quiet. "Well, what now?" asked Grandpa, clearly a little impatient.

"You ask me what that means," I said. "Grandma always does it that way."

"Your grandma should know," he said. "She has gone through this often enough, I fear."

"Grandma says you aren't always serious about hearing my lessons."

"Oh, she does?" asked Grandpa. "Well, that's all right. Women may be serious, but men are profound." His fingers fiddled with the edges of his newspaper.

"I'm afraid you just mix me up, *Bestefar*," I said.

"Well, we do share that in common," he said. "Why don't you say your lessons to your grandmother when she comes home? You'll probably have to anyway." He stroked his goatee thoughtfully. I eased the Catechism gently out of his free hand, lest he quickly change his mind.

"Do you miss Norway?" I asked, searching quickly for a subject safely removed from Martin Luther and his academic mind.

"Miss Norway?" asked Grandpa, peering foggily around the edge of the *Skandinaven* he was beginning to peruse.

"Did you personally see Grieg?" I persisted.

"Did I what? *Ja, ja vist.*"

"Did you really build his summer home?"

Down came the *Skandinaven*. "So we have finished with the Catechism, have we?"

"I thought so," I replied meekly. "You began to read the paper.

"Grandpa, tell me about the summer you built Grieg's summer home. Dode can play a little Grieg," I offered brightly.

Grandpa shook his gray head. "I have told you the story so often, you could well tell me."

"I get mixed up. Was it above the fjord?"

"Well, it certainly wasn't in it."

"How big?"

"Not many rooms. Just a place where he could compose and study. With Grieg's big piano in front of a window overlooking the fjord."

"How big?"

"*Det ved jeg intet.* I don't know. The biggest I have ever seen."

"Why did you build his house?"

"Well, why shouldn't I have built it?" he retorted. "I was the only builder on our side of the fjord."

"I thought you ran a sawmill."

"In the winters I ran a sawmill. In the summer I farmed and did general contracting."

"Did you think that Grieg was a strange man? You told me once you did."

"I did?" asked Grandpa, mildly surprised. "Well, maybe so. It is easy to call a man peculiar if he but differs slightly from us." His face brightened visibly. "Why don't you run out in the snow and play?" he suggested.

"Will you tell *Bestemor* that you heard my lessons?" I asked.

Grandpa picked up his paper. "Indeed I will. I will tell her that you not only knew the answers this afternoon but could ask the questions as well. Now," said Grandpa with a slight show of impatience, "will you please put your overshoes on, or I shall go down in the cellar and read as I have often done before when women and their prattle would not give me peace."

Grandpa, descendant of Vikings whose base had once been the Hardanger Fjord, was never happier than when traveling; and Grandma insisted she was never happier than when she slept and ate upon a train. And of course an eight-year-old child was often just happy.

So it was easy for Uncle Henry to persuade my grandparents to spend another winter in Tucson. Aunt Gudrun and Monsey cat moved in with Aunt Tina, and we closed our house for the winter. I stroked the trunk of every cottonwood and willow tree in a good-by caress, and left a message to myself to be read upon my return in spring.

When the time came to entrain, *Bestefar*, being a Norwegian man, had the lower berth. Grandma and I climbed to the upper, where she hoped to keep me from falling out. In Minneapolis Grandpa was met in the station by a minister who wore his collar backward and talked fluently about his mission to convert the Jews. Grandma and I strolled contentedly about the huge station, savoring the smell of popcorn, watching the hurrying crowds, and peeking out timidly at the honking traffic swirling by.

Finally the Rock Island train steamed into the dome-covered tracks; and we were sitting in a dusty-smelling Pullman rolling through the twin cities. We crawled across the high bridge spanning the Mississippi, with little boats puffing far below us and smoke belching out of myriads of high chimneys. Farther on grimy-faced boys from grimy shacks threw stones at the clicking wheels, and tired-looking women threw wash water out back doors.

When dusk arrived the rolling countryside, covered with patches of snow, turned into a glowing blush pink, and clumps of bare trees in the draws threw long shadows against the cone-shaped hills.

The next morning Grandma delivered her version of train etiquette. "Sit still as much as humanly possible. If you must walk up the aisle, talk to no one except to say hello if someone speaks to you first. It's all right to smile," she said as an afterthought, "if someone should smile at you."

To avert any unnecessary social contacts, Grandma came copiously supplied with reading material. Chief among her offerings were, of course, a Norwegian primer and the omnipresent Catechism, impossible to lose even on a moving train. Faced with the choice of memorizing a book sixteenth-century Luther had written to torment unborn generations of children or the privilege of watching the passing landscape, I found it relatively simple to prefer the latter.

Three or four days of inactivity were an educational challenge Grandma could not overlook. What better time to keep on memorizing this little brown book with its capsulelike answers to the riddle of the universe? So Grandma sat, a stern little statue of a teacher, making me recite memorized quotations. Disconcerted by the incredulous stares of passengers walking by our seat, I ducked my head and delivered myself of quotations. "Please can I walk again?" I asked, tiring.

"If you remember to conduct yourself properly," allowed Grandma.

At the end of the car I was waylaid by two smiling
women.

"Whatever were you chattering back there, child?" asked one of them, patting the front of her pink chiffon blouse after hiding a handkerchief in its lovely depths.

"Luther's Catechism," I said, holding my hand on the back of the red plush seat and swinging my foot against its base.

"Lord! In Russian?" asked the black-haired one.

"No, in Norwegian," I replied obediently.

"Whatever for?" she asked.

"For Grandma."

"But why in Norwegian?" she persisted.

"So Grandma can explain about God. She doesn't know all the words in English. And in Sunday school I'll learn it in English for the preacher."

"Well, I'll be a . . . !" gasped the one in pink chiffon. By now Grandma was at the water cooler, trying to look pleasant to the strangers and at the same time stern toward me.

"Come," she said. "I think you have told enough. Exshus me," she said, turning to the startled women, "if my little child has bothered you." She nodded politely and took me firmly by the hand. "Why don't you go and sit down and count telephone poles again?" she suggested.

In Kansas City Grandpa explained that an unseasonal thaw had flooded several miles of land and inundated bridges; so we were forced to reroute on a slow train that moved leisurely across the gentle rolling plains of Kansas and gave wonderful glimpses into the private lives of people who lived on farms surrounded by stone fences.

"That man just came out of his backhouse," I giggled
to Grandma, who looked up from her church paper in

time to see the stranger in question hitch up his trousers.

"*For sind og skam!* For sin and shame!" she scolded. "If you feel that lively, you can take out your Catechism and memorize a brand-new bedtime prayer."

Grandma began to fret because she was sure Uncle Henry would worry when our scheduled train rolled in without us.

But Grandpa, buried in sheaves of timetables and reading matter, dismissed the matter lightly. "What of it?" he countered. "If one train doesn't bring us, they know another will."

"But Nellie," worried Grandma, "you know how *she* can fuss when things go wrong."

"Leave it to me," suggested Grandpa grandly.

A day later the train we had caught in El Paso rolled into the old station near the west end of Congress Street. It was dark and crowding midnight.

After Grandpa and the porter had stacked our luggage on one end of the long bench Grandma said, "What shall we do, Ole? There is no one here to meet us."

Grandpa pulled out his big gold watch from a vest pocket. I pushed the red velvet poke bonnet off my head and sat down to await the consummation of their friendly argument. "It is too late to disturb anyone," he conceded, "even our own son."

Grandma frowned with weariness. "I'd disturb no one." She sat beside me, pale and tired, yet not reminding Grandpa that it was his decision which placed us all in such a predicament.

"A hotel?" he asked.

86 "Nellie would never forgive us," Grandma said. She

stroked my hair. "Try to sleep, *du vesle*, you little one," she comforted, making a nest in her lap for my head. I lay there entranced by the people in the station.

Indians dozed on an opposite bench. A chattering Mexican family flitted past, exclaiming loudly over a sheaf of tickets. Air that seemed unbelievably mild after a Dakota winter blew keen and fresh through the drafty station. A barrel-shaped Indian squaw, her hair knotted intricately with a bright red ribbon, put a laundry-size bundle upon the floor, sat upon it, and stared absorbedly at nothing. A freight thundered into the station, shook the bench on which we sat, rattled to a screeching stop. The big clock on the wall slowly wound its minute hand. The strong repulsive odor from a nearby spittoon saturated the air.

"If we fall asleep will those dark people take our luggage?" I asked, with the racial intolerance one group often has toward another.

Grandma stroked my hair. "*Nei vist*," she said, "have you forgotten God created us all? Or that two years ago when you were here you played with the Mexican consul's children next door to your Uncle Henry's?"

In the morning I awakened to find Grandpa patiently holding me in his arms and nodding fitfully.

"How did you like sleeping in a railroad station?" he asked, coming awake with a start. Grandma was asleep, her head resting on a suitcase.

Grandpa and I tiptoed out to the front. In the east the sky was paling. The sharp odor of rain-washed greasewood permeated the air, and small puddles of water filled low places on the cement. Grandpa inhaled deeply.

"It's good to be back," he commented, straightening

his shoulders and breathing deeply of the creosote-smelling air. "When the café opens, we shall go across and have some pancakes," he promised. "And before long the streetcars will be running."

When we returned to the waiting room Grandma was sitting up, looking terribly abashed at doing such a personal thing as awakening in a public room. "Where have you two been?" she demanded crisply. "I began to think you had gone." She drew the palms of her hands across her neatly parted hair. Grandpa began frequent excursions to the front of the station. Finally he hurried back with the air of one who has had too much of waiting for womenfolk.

"Come!" he commanded. "The café is now open. We must have our breakfast." Without further ado he picked up the two heaviest suitcases and left Grandma and me to stagger after him with our wraps and two small grips.

"If that isn't like Ole," commented Grandma with early morning touchiness, "coming to spend the whole winter in Tucson and rushing headlong after a plate of pancakes!"

Several yards ahead Grandpa strode impatiently toward the beckoning windows of a small café. When he got to the street he waited resignedly, as one might wait for an exploring poodle to catch up with its master.

"Come," he said, "there's no need to loiter at the curb." In the café, he stacked our baggage beside the counter and nodded us to seats.

"Pancakes, bacon, and coffee for all," he ordered.

"But, Ole," said Grandma, remembering four successive mornings of waffles or pancakes, served in dining cars or busy station cafés, "maybe we don't want pancakes."

"What's better than pancakes?" asked Grandpa with true Scandinavian prejudice. "Besides, we have no time to waste deciding what we shall eat. Any minute now the streetcar will be coming."

The owner stood poised above his smoking griddle, studying our strange flow of language as though we were creatures dropped by the night's rain. When Grandpa fell silent he ladled scoops of batter upon the waiting griddle and turned to pour the coffee.

Grandma, whose stomach was more sensitive than Grandpa's perceptions regarding the female mind, sighed resignedly and stared forlornly at the stack of cakes the man set before her. Grandpa was eating with the kind of relish he reserved only for hotcakes and waffles. Left to my own devices, I helped myself generously from a besmirched syrup bottle. Grandma stirred her coffee listlessly and reached for her pat of butter.

Halfway through his stack of pancakes, Grandpa cocked his head to one side and said, "Guro, I think I hear the streetcar." He eyed her untouched food. "You'll have to be ready."

Ordinarily docile and subscribing to the superiority of the male—the Norwegian variety, at least—Grandma rewarded *Bestefar* with a venomous stare and poured a dash of syrup on her stack.

Far down the street rose a clamor and a clanking. Grandpa turned in his seat and stared out the dusty window. "Here she comes!" he warned. Grandpa took a bill from his wallet and handed it to the proprietor. Then he wiped his mustache upon a napkin and announced that he was now ready to leave.

"I have only now begun to eat," persisted Grandma, pushing a pancake around the plate with her fork.

"You have heard the car," insisted Grandpa stubbornly. He began to pick up the baggage stacked beside him. The proprietor handed him his change. "Streetcars and trains don't wait," argued Grandpa, pocketing the coins.

"There are others," said Grandma, taking a sip of coffee.

Bestefar sniffed, stroked his goatee. "I intend to get up to the house before my son leaves for his office," said Grandpa grandly. "You and Nellie can drink coffee all day once you get there."

Grandma, now fully embarrassed by the interest the plump café man evinced in an argument he could not understand but could clearly see, put down her fork and got up. I followed. She picked up a light valise and nodded for me to follow.

Grandpa was across the street by now, waiting by the car stop and regarding his female contingent with amused disgust. We caught up with him as he was about to embark.

He ushered us in before him. "I thought you would come to your senses," he said.

1

Aunt Nellie   "All Swedes have a yellow streak around their stomach," Grandpa often remarked, carrying on the conventional, though friendly, rivalry between Swedes and Norwegians.

Uncle Henry's wife, Aunt Nellie, was Swedish, though

I was unable ever to discover whether she possessed what Grandpa described as standard equipment.

According to her in-laws, especially the skirted group, Aunt Nellie was often described as difficult to get along with. Years later I made the simple discovery that anyone even slightly different from other women is often considered a pariah by her own sex, which likes to apply a standard set of answers to a standard set of problems.

It was true that Aunt Nellie washed every bit of canned goods that entered her kitchen, with naphtha soap. "People come to Tucson for their health," she explained. "Even some of our food handlers are sick. Why should I store their germs on my pantry shelf?" So even Ling's vegetables, bought directly from his wagon drawn by a lazy horse, were taken in and scrubbed to enamel shininess. Tomatoes were singed over the gas flame, and the peeling quickly drawn off before slicing.

So careful was Aunt Nellie that she maintained a sterile drainboard on the left side of the sink and an unsterile on the right, where unwashed dishes, canned goods, and vegetables were placed. Woe to the helper—big or little—who placed a can of corn fresh from the store on the sterile side!

Aunt Gudrun, in speaking of Aunt Nellie's fetish on this subject, probably summed up the female family-consensus when she tossed her bright head and said, "Pooh! Who can spend her time bothering with ideas like that? I can find a better way to spend my time, and eat well too."

But a child rather enjoyed such a controversial kitchen.

92 I pictured the germs on the unsterile side marching up

and down, racing with glee, and clinging precariously to the edge of a can before their final plunge into soapy water and a scalding torrent from a teakettle. On the sterile side, washed cups and saucers, gleaming as they did nowhere else, it seemed, rested from their ordeal by scalding water and waited to be placed on the polar whiteness of a damask tablecloth.

That was the way it was at Aunt Nellie's, and that was the way we found it the morning after our fitful sleep in a Southern Pacific railroad station. Grandpa's imperious push on the front doorbell brought a surprised Aunt Nellie and Uncle Henry to the front door.

Uncle Henry, after the initial shock, shook his head in disbelief that his aging parents and their young charge would spend the night in a public waiting room, while Aunt Nellie insisted again and again in her heavy Swedish brogue that she couldn't understand why they hadn't been called on the telephone, no matter what the hour.

The back door slammed, footsteps crossed the back porch and kitchen, and in came my red-haired brother Carl. Before he shook hands with his grandparents he took quick inventory of his little sister in the furtive but thoroughly comprehensive way all boys of that age study girls at this age. Soon we were eying each other in the typically cold appraisal of childhood. Grandma, understandably relieved to be free of her restless charge, suggested we go outside and play. In the grape arbor at the back of the house Carl fidgeted with odds and ends of twine, sticks, and adolescent treasure; and then suddenly welcomed my return to the Southwest with a stiff little 93 poke in the ribs. I knew, in the unspoken language of childhood, that we were on firm footing again, despite my two years' absence from Tucson.

On my first day of school the principal gave me a surprisingly warm welcome after I had been introduced by Aunt Nellie as Uncle Sven's niece from North Dakota. It seemed that the slender brunette Miss Powers had once been a girl friend of Uncle Sven's, during his stay in Tucson.

Consequently, when the bell rang to summon us in, I was able to bask in the unexpected limelight of a generous, toothy smile from Miss Powers. Often through the year, when our eager little feet lined up to march in to music played by an anemic stick of a blonde banging an old piano near the stair railing, the principal would draw me aside and ask, "What do you hear from your Uncle Sven up in North Dakota?" Years later, when I heard that she had married a German immigrant taken to trial for espionage after World War I, I wondered why she had wandered into such an alliance when at one time she might have had my Uncle Sven. As a go-between for parted lovers, I had certainly failed to do my part.

At Uncle Henry's the days passed pleasantly, with Aunt Nellie quite sure that I was too young to understand the germ theory that ruled her kitchen. Still, she had help enough without me, since she had two other guests that winter besides my grandparents and me, two of her Swedish cousins from Nebraska, who were teaching in the Tucson schools. Amy and Anna Nelson had the quiet dignity and the friendly charm often found among Swedish women. My brother, who had been trained to know and respect the clean and the unclean drainboards, was often recruited to help. Thus Aunt Nellie, who had once been William Jennings Bryan's cook, was amply encouraged to load the big table with roasts of sirloin of beef, crown roasts of pork, and crusty legs of lamb.

After one of her filling dinners, eaten leisurely under the big swinging green-glass-shaded lamp, Uncle Henry often drew me to his lap before his big roll-top desk in the corner, where I was encouraged to share the great learning I had acquired that day in the third grade, or where I drew pictures for him on a pad of scratch paper. Like Grandma, he possessed a quiet iron will underneath a briskly pleasant exterior; and any word of praise he gave me was a seed upon the heart to grow blossoms of remembrance.

Aunt Nellie took it upon herself to supervise my evening bath. Naturally she gave me the same brisk treatment she gave a piece of crockery in her kitchen, knowing places back of ears and around knuckles where the offending and busy germ population possessed a metropolitan strength.

By the time I was ready for bed my Dakota white skin was scrubbed to apple-blossom pinkness. Bedded down on her sleeping porch (she had quickly explained to Grandma that it was unhealthful for the very young to sleep with the very old), I snuggled under gray and red Swedish homespun blankets. Grandma slipped in quietly to hear my prayers; and when she had closed the porch door in her gentle, unobtrusive way I lay there listening to the night sounds of Tucson: the clanking and squeaking of the streetcar on Third Street, a half block away, the dry rustle of grapevines outside the porch window, and the

95 puffing blasts of Southern Pacific trains on the tracks a

half mile south of the house. Every sound was magnified in the chilly, dry air.

The stars in the black night outside winked and receded, sparkled and changed. Loneliness wrapped me in, like a stiff, suffocating blanket, and I remembered Uncle's frequent bantering "We'll keep Margaret here when you leave in the spring." To make sure that God understood how much I needed Grandpa and Grandma, I made a pact with Him. First I counted to one hundred in Norwegian, then I counted to one hundred in English, always fearing that before I finished I might fall asleep and awaken to find my gentle grandparents gone. Let the modern psychologist call it a compulsion neurosis or what he will, this nightly abracadabra served as a log in the river of childish uncertainty to which I could cling. The train bells rang, the freights on the sidings chortled and puffed, the voices of loved ones rose and fell in the house at my back; but I fell asleep in a new land, sure of both God and my grandparents.

During long sunny afternoons I often played with the children next door, daughters of the consul from Sonora, Mexico. At the back of their lot, in a little cottage, lived their peon servant and her black-eyed daughter Carlotta, with a sharp little vixen face and a manner alternating between groveling compliancy and sharp outbursts of hate. She did not attend school, but spent her monotonous days fetching and carrying for her servant mother, munching hungrily on our crumbs of approval.

One afternoon when school had been dismissed, I walked up Third Avenue toward Uncle's white stucco house. Several feet ahead, my path was blocked by two 96 older schoolgirls.

"You're new here," they warned, "and we say you can't walk on our street, ever!"

"But I live here now!" I protested with third-grade meekness.

"We say you stay off this street, forever!" Two blond heads bent to pick up stones, of which Tucson had such a plentiful supply. Large protruding teeth gleamed sadistically in twin faces. "We'll stone you to pieces if you just once set foot on our street again!" They fled in bursts of exaggerated laughter.

Neither Grandma nor the brown Catechism had ever taught me directly how to cope with a situation like this, except to turn the other cheek and get stoned from two exposures instead of one. Every day I worried through my lessons in school and, when evening came, I ventured on new and completely strange streets in an effort to avoid my tormentors, coming home later and later.

And then one evening Grandma waited for me at the pomegranate hedge, nervously scanning the alley for my return. "Where have you been?" she demanded sternly.

"Well, I just now came home from school," I lied, not knowing how I could explain the existence of two unearned enemies.

"You have lied, and a lie is a sin I have never been able to countenance." She shook her head sadly. "I know that you have lied because the girls next door have been home for over a half hour." Scrutinizing my face, Grandma saw only a willful and pugnacious stubbornness. "Well, there's no help for it. I shall have to switch you."

My freckled brother slunk around the corner of the
house as though he wished to escape the pain vicariously,

giving me a sympathetic glance that seemed to telegraph that he, too, had learned of the cruelty of adults.

Grandma took me firmly by the hand and led me into Uncle's woodshed, where stacked piles of mesquite waiting for the fireplace gave off a dusty, faintly sweet aroma. As she reached for the family switch lying upon a stack of corded wood, her face twisted with pain. Sharp little cracks burst like fire on my black sateen bloomers, and tears stung at my face.

For a moment Grandma's hand was raised, while she apparently deliberated whether I had had enough to do any good. As I looked up, I saw Carlotta's sharp little face grin wickedly through a little hole in the siding. Her teeth gleamed, and her black eyes crackled with light.

I turned on Grandma like a blond fury. "You can't switch me with *her* standing there laughing!" I screamed. "Don't you dare try it again! Don't you dare!" All the ignominy of running from my tormentors and of being the butt of Carlotta's twisted pleasure made me turn on Grandma. She regarded me with complete and startled amazement; and then she sat down on the nearest stack of wood and burst into tears.

"Ja, I'm too old to be raising a family," she said sadly. "I'm afraid I no longer feel sure of myself, nor even that I am doing the right thing." So Grandma and I sat in the warm woodshed, crying over a world that was often too lopsided for human comfort.

But afternoons were not always like that. Often I'd find Grandma waiting for me on the front porch, dressed in her good black wool skirt and a crisp white blouse, to take me walking with her. "Visitors should never be too much underfoot," she remarked, taking my hand and starting down the sidewalk, past Uncle's small brown stone retaining wall. "Women like to order their own kitchens."

So we set out upon afternoon walks, sometimes toward the university campus, often downtown. At the end of the first block Grandma ordered Spot, Uncle's white and brown terrier, home again. He listened to her Norwegian commands with perfect respect, eyed us as though we were simple to reject his surveillance, and then started home with a stiff, offended trot. Several blocks away we came upon Spot, sitting on a corner and waiting for us to catch up with him. Patiently Grandma scolded him again. Studying her to see whether Grandma's facial expressions matched her strange flow of words, Spot held his ground. Finally, failing to win her over with friendly exploring gestures at her feet, he trotted home with an air of injured disgrace.

We continued toward town, crossing the Fourth Avenue arroyo on a rickety suspension bridge which swung back and forth with each footfall. On the banks of the arroyo stood a scattering of adobe huts occupied by Mexicans and Chinese. Short, squat Chinese women, hobbling like marionettes on bound feet, moved impassively about their tasks.

Grandma always shook her head in a frightfully sad way after such an encounter. "They're heathen," she remarked, "enslaved to ignorant customs and superstitions." Across the arroyo we often passed a Pima Indian woman sitting content among her stacks of red-brown pottery and puffing quietly on a clay pipe. Again Grandma shook her head over the wickedness of the world. "If she must smoke," she sighed, "why must she choose one of the busiest streets?"

"But, *Bestemor*," I often teased, "Grandpa said once some of the women in Norway smoked, and pipes, too!" I skipped in front of her, turned, nodded affirmation. "He really did!"

"Maybe they did," she replied tartly, "but I never saw them even if your grandpa did."

Down in front of Kresge's dime store waited Spot, a confusing mixture of pride at his own cleverness and fear of banishment. By now Grandma was partially resigned. He had come this far, hadn't he? Still, she made a futile effort to send him home, in compliance with Aunt Nellie's strict orders.

In the dime store Grandma looked for some small household gift to take to Aunt Nellie. That done, she moved slowly up and down the aisles with an air of a female Socrates seeming to declare, "How much there is in this world I should not care to possess!"

At Stone Avenue we turned north, no sign anywhere of our peripatetic little companion. Grandma's downtown itinerary always took her past Uncle's architect's office; and sometimes she would stop, at other times merely stroll by, seeming to be governed by an intuitive sense whether to disturb her son or walk quietly on.

When we did stop, Uncle always met us with a happy smile and the remark, "I knew you were coming. Spot has already been at the back door announcing a family arrival." I stood there enchanted by the tall tables for the draftsmen, the big wastepaper baskets overflowing with discarded blueprints, and the sketches of building elevations hanging upon the walls.

Demure and always afraid of being in the way, Grandma was still unable to conceal her huge love for and delight in her oldest son; and when she left, her face seemed to bear an expression that justified her years of childbearing, her hardships upon land and sea. I always clutched a new pencil in my hand or a shiny nickel to spend in some shop on the way home. Outside in the darkening crisp air Grandma chided me to sudden haste, as though the journey were now over. "There's much I can do to help Nellie," she said.

At the back door of Uncle's house, many blocks later, rested Spot, watching us with an air of superiority for having reached home with a dexterity that put two-legged creatures to shame. In the grape arbor sat Tom, Aunt Nellie's occasional handy man, muttering to himself through a heavy black beard, and eating his supper from a discarded coffee tin. Black-eyed and shaggy, often incredibly dirty, Tom had the bearing of a man of distinction. "He once studied for the priesthood in Mexico," explained Grandma. "You must treat him with respect," she warned; and then added, with true Lutheran bias, "still, maybe he's better off as a beggar, anyway."

The coffee can, as Tom's dinner plate, was truly an invention only an Aunt Nellie could have devised. Emptied of coffee grounds and scrubbed to meet her rigid standards, it was as clean as one of her dinner plates when she handed it to Tom. When the old man had finished his meal and had muttered his way across the darkening yard to a shack beside the railroad tracks, the coffee can was picked up gingerly and tossed into the garbage. The supply of coffee cans, in a household where coffee was the morning's song and the late evening's benediction, was, of course, inexhaustible.

When spring came, and it came early in southern Arizona, Grandma talked frequently of returning to Grand Prairie. "I shall never forget the summers I spent here," she said, with a shudder at the memory, "and I have no wish to repeat the misery."

"When we asked Margaret to stay with us when she was six," laughed Aunt Nellie, who was one of those adults prone to repeat children's witticisms, without or with encouragement, "do you remember how she lisped, 'I don't like Arithona. Ith's nothin' but sthand, sthage, and sthunshine'?" I was restless for Grand Prairie, too, wondering whether Aunt Gudrun had persisted in her maidenly status, whether Monsey had forgotten me, and feeling lonesome for the gray house between the grove of willows and the protecting fringe of cottonwoods.

"Before you leave, we're going to have a picnic," promised Aunt Nellie, "and we'll go to Oracle!"

"We haven't taken Margaret to Oracle since those years she was here as a baby," remarked Uncle Henry, who had a true bent for anything statistical.

Aunt Nellie's kitchen became the scene of frenzied preparations for a Sunday's outing. Aunt Nellie, Grandma, and the two mild-mannered schoolteachers all got in each other's way preparing and packing food which was to keep us alive for one day.

No one in Aunt Nellie's kitchen ever did anything except in Aunt Nellie's prescribed way (unless, perhaps, Aunt Gudrun, when she was there); and there was much rewashing and rewrapping of food, a great many orders delivered and redelivered in Aunt Nellie's deep-voiced and commanding Swedish.

From the big black coal range came a pot of bubbling baked beans, sprouting hunks of succulent pork simmering in rich brown juice. Aunt Nellie took layers and layers of bleached germ-free toweling and wrapped this around the wide-mouthed bean crock.

When Carl had been sent on enough errands to have traversed the distance to Oracle and back, by foot; when I had been silenced again and again by flustered little Grandma; and when Uncle Henry had been scolded for male sins of omission and commission pertaining to the packing of the car, we were finally ready to leave for Oracle, on the other side of Tucson's Santa Catalina Mountains.

In the front seat of Uncle's touring car rode Aunt Nellie, beside him, and my brother Carl with his head hanging over the door gasping for that extra air so necessary for the survival of boys and dogs. In the back seat I sat upon Amy's lap, with Grandma at one side and Anna upon the other. In another car rode Grandpa, along with the preacher and his temporal kin, as well as the German professor and his comfortable wife from the university, invited not for any intellectual stimulus, probably, but for the happy fact that they, too, were Lutherans.

On Amy's lap I had a high bouncing view of the swelling foothills climbing to the pine-covered Catalinas. The warm April air sang in our ears, the nose of the little car scented the upward trail, and the schoolteachers chatted happily on both sides, Grandma chiming in occasionally with quiet acquiescence.

"Won't you be glad to see your sisters in Grand Prairie again?" asked Anna in the bright conversational tone used exclusively for small children.

"Especially her big sister Bertina," added Amy, with arm tight about my waist.

"I guess so," I admitted, "and I hope she has improved."

"Improved? What do you mean?" asked Anna, trying to balance a cake pan on her lap and keep her sailor hat anchored to her blond head.

"I hope she's not as sassy as she used to be," I explained.

"I thought she was a nice girl," encouraged Anna, winking at Amy.

"Just terrible," I said, ignoring Grandma's look of sudden surprise. "Auntie doesn't know what to do with her at times," I continued, warming up to the subject. "She's really a problem, and I don't think Aunt Tina likes her at times."

"I'm sure she does," said Amy, trying to keep me anchored to her lap in spite of my wriggling and the wild bouncing of the climbing car. Large cotton clouds floated decoratively in the bright spring sky. Paths of newly sprung flowers in pale yellows and warm orange nodded to us as the car chugged by. The north side of the Catalinas loomed large and massive, flitting shadows marking cacti-peppered uplands and darkening deep canyons.

I shifted around to regard the affectionate Amy with love and interest. "You see, Aunt Tina would never adopt Bertina," I continued, "and she leaves her all the dishes to do after school and makes her work harder and harder all the time. It's pitiful!"

104 "Magrit!" cracked Grandma's voice in my ear.

Grandma looked at the teachers, each in turn, with a humble and apologetic air. "She gets carried away at times," she explained. "I have the hardest time getting her to distinguish between fancy and fact. Too many fairy stories," she apologized. "Children are really better off reading Bible stories."

"Well, we're almost there," said Uncle Henry, who had the happy knack of driving with his face turned to the side of the road, especially when the road was scenic as well as precipitous.

Aunt Nellie turned toward us. "I can hardly wait for a taste of those good baked beans! I know they're going to be good."

Gaining altitude constantly, the car chugged and sputtered, climbing the circuitous road that skirted overhanging boulders, brushed against juniper branches and manzanita bushes. The air had the pungent sharpness of higher desert elevations.

Uncle Henry turned the car off the narrow road into a little draw shaded by oak trees, dripping with the parasitic growth of mistletoe. "Well," he said, opening the door beside him, "we beat the other car up here!"

Aunt Nellie was out and already presiding over her outdoor kitchen. "Let's get the lunch out!" she ordered. "Everyone's hungry." I began to wriggle off Amy's lap. She had been sitting effusively admiring the scenery, sniffing at the air, but still holding me firmly about the waist.

Aunt Nellie opened the rear door at our feet and reached for the towel-enclosed crock of beans. She threw her hands up into the air and emitted a wail of horror and despair.

"My beans! My beautiful beans!" she cried, reaching into the stacked depths at our feet. With outstretched arms she staggered from the car, the bean pot extended into the air. "Look here!" she wailed. "Just look here! Someone has ridden the whole way up here with her feet in my beans!" An outraged wail burst from her large, full lips.

Grandma and Amy and Anna all looked at me. "Well, it *was* covered with dish towels," said the professor's stubby little wife, who had arrived during the debacle. "It should be all right," she insisted, looking from one woman to another with an air of convincing tact.

Aunt Nellie regarded her *pièce de résistance* with a penetrating but anguished look. "No-o-o," she said finally, "we can't serve the beans." The towel had slipped a little, and the beans were uncovered. They looked as if they had been tromped down. "No," she said, giving the crock a parting glance. "The beans we'll not use. How could we ever be sure they were not full of germs?"

I fled to Grandpa, whose face was a mixture of solicitude for me and repressed laughter.

Aunt Nellie came toward us. "Come, Margaret," she said in a supreme gesture of culinary sacrifice. "Come, you and I will go up on the hillside and feed the beans to hungry birds."

12

Knitting for the Cat   Late in April the morning train left us standing upon the wooden platform in Grand Prairie. "You missed a hard winter," said Uncle Thorvald, herding us into the seven-passenger Buick standing beside the yellow depot. Melting drifts, stained with dark veins of snow and smudged with patches of mud, showed that winter was loath to concede a victory to approaching May.

"The girls slid off the garage roof to a snowbank," said Uncle with the pride of a Northerner for the hardships he endures. "Just got the car out of the garage last week," he bragged, helping Grandpa stow our baggage into the car. "Good thing you didn't return any sooner."

"How is Christina?" asked Grandma anxiously.

"All right. As well as can be expected," answered Uncle Thorvald.

"You better drive us straight home," suggested Grandpa. "No sense in bothering you people."

"I should say not!" retorted Uncle. "Just started your furnace this morning. It's going to take a day or two to chase all the cold out, it's had all winter to settle. Felt like an icehouse down there."

Grandpa, who could never see any sense to going anywhere else when the windows of home beckoned, looked slightly disappointed. Grandma sat on the back seat, entirely disregarding me until she discovered that I was pulling out one of the folding seats in front of us. "For *skam!*" she scolded. "Learn to keep your hands off others' property."

In the kitchen at Uncle Thorvald's house Aunt Tina gave us a warm hug and a huge welcome, while Grandma and she dabbed at escaping tears. I stared at Aunt Tina with amazement. What one winter had done to her! When Grandma took me upstairs to the bathroom to wash off the dust and smudge of travel, I whispered, "Did Aunt Tina eat too much?"

"Hush!" warned Grandma. "Don't make any personal remarks to her—not one! You must not say a single word to her about growing fat, do you hear?"

Grandma's admonitions were largely lost in the excitement taking place downstairs. Aunt Gudrun was there! The girls, my sisters, were home for lunch, and Monsey cat had been let out of the basement. I embraced Aunt Gudrun and the girls, picked up the purring cat. There was enough excitement to last for a day, even for an eight-year-old.

All through dinner I stared at them: Aunt Gudrun looking so much the same, I was sure she could not have married; Dode, whose freckles had faded during the winter months but whose hair had not; Dally, now in high school, and sitting thoughtful and composed by the kitchen door for errands of the table. But most of all I stared at Aunt Tina, plump, self-absorbed, a little smug, as she helped herself to roast and potatoes.

"Tak for maten, thank you," said Grandpa when the meal was over. "Now, Guro," he said, turning to Grandma, "if you can't be of any help here, I'd suggest we go quickly to our own house."

"There is nothing to do here," said Aunt Tina. "The girls have stacked the dishes and will clean up the kitchen when school is out. But we haven't visited, Mother!" she protested, giving her father a mildly indignant glance.

Grandma gave her spouse an uncertain look. "Women always can visit," urged Grandpa, nudging Bestemor toward our wraps in the chilly hall.

"Well, Thorvald will get your luggage down to you," said Aunt Christina, accompanying us slowly to the hallway. "We haven't talked at all, Mother, but I'll be down later."

"No, truly," remonstrated Grandma. "That you won't, with the ground slippery and wet. You'll wait until I get up here again. I'll have your father settled soon, once he has a look around our house again."

Down in our house beside the willow grove Monsey trailed after us, wailing disconsolately through the unaired chilly rooms, brushing against my legs in outbursts of unselfish affection, and wailing again to remind us of months of neglect and separation from familiar, loved surroundings.

Grandpa was down in the basement shaking the furnace with an enthusiasm only a winter in the South could have engendered. Grandma, in complete disregard of the operations in the cellar, opened every other window and lamented the stale air.

Upstairs in the bedroom I shared with Aunt Gudrun, I stood in the very center of the room, taking ecstatic inventory of humble and familiar surroundings. Through the low window beyond, I saw the willows standing deep in melted snow water, the field to my right wet and black and rich, awaiting a warm day for the garden plow. The ungraded street beside our fence was a rutted lane, greening beside patches of snow that lined it. Far down the street I saw the roof of the Rekve Store, where Uncle Thorvald had gone to work after leaving us at the front gate.

I walked over to the sliding door that gave entry to a
miniature storage attic. Feeling about in the dusty dark, I

came upon a little shoebox, from which I extracted a much-folded note.

"Dear Margarethe Henrickson," I began to read aloud. In all secret correspondence I assumed my grandfather's name.

When you read this [I went on] you'll be qwite old. Plese dont forget how you felt in Novembre when you left for Tuscon and that you praid Aunt Gudrun wuold never git maried and that nothing would kill off Gramma. Nor Granpa. I am writeing this on a dark windey day. It is butiful, and the sownd of it is butiful, and I dont like to go to Tuscon.
Yours truley,
Mugs
P.s. If somthing shuould hapen to me, burn this up who ever you are.

So that was how I had felt! I sat on the edge of the duster-covered bed and sighed over the passage of time. Grandpa's voice rose loud and scolding through the register in the floor. I thrust the note into my apron pocket. "Close that window up there! Do you hear me?" he yelled. "Only women would be fools enough to open up all the windows at the same time you heat a house!" I drew the window down with a loud bang to let Grandpa know how hastily I had complied with his wishes.

"But, Ole," I heard Grandma say in her gentle voice, "musty air never heats like fresh air." But Grandpa's steps were already on the sidewalk below my window. He was going after the *Skandinaven*.

In school that spring I discovered that not even a recent trip to Arizona could compete with the importance a new 110 girl in class assumed. She was small-boned, lithe, gay, pugnacious, pretty—I sat frozen with envy and despair. Her provocative upper lip showed small even teeth; and when she wasn't smiling she was chattering. The girls who had always walked home from school with me now clustered admiringly around Janice. It was more than I could bear.

"Haven't you gotten acquainted with Dr. Saylor's little girl?" prodded Aunt Gudrun one evening.

"I've seen her," I admitted, with what I hoped was a convincing disinterest.

"He's our new dentist. They're lovely people. It would be nice to make friends with Janice."

So at night I wadded a piece of paper into a large ball and placed it inside my upper lip, with the hope that by morning some glorious metamorphosis would have occurred so that I, too, could reward my teacher's attentions with a toothy little smile.

"My father is the only dentist in town," I heard Janice tell Miss Wiley one afternoon, "and he'd just love to fix your teeth or clean them or whatever you need done." I stood sliding an eraser up and down its chalky little track and wondering what equally kind thing I could do for the slender Miss Wiley. I could hardly say, "Grandpa will build you an end table in his basement workshop," for what would Miss Wiley do with a table, living across from the school in a rented room!

"Well, let's go," said Janice, beckoning to a group of admiring third-graders. "People from Arizona can't join this gang," she teased.

I wanted to explain that I had lived in Grand Prairie long before she came; but the pretty little vixen was off,

skipping down the sidewalk with a saucy toss of her brown bobbed hair. I was sorry now that I had gone to Tucson.

When school had been out for a few weeks and I had no competitive worries to annoy me, Dode and I were playing hide-and-seek one day under the spirea bushes banked against Uncle Thorvald's house. The sound of deep sobbing came from the open living-room windows, with intermittent soothing remarks from Grandma. "What's the matter, Dode?" I whispered, with the sudden fright children feel when the adult world proves to be imperfect.

"It's nothing you would understand," said Dode, sticking her Irish-looking little face above a spirea sprig. "It's just the way Aunt Tina feels these days. That's all."

"Maybe she's been working too hard knitting clothes for the cat," I said.

"She's not knitting clothes for the *cat!*" scoffed Dode.

"I didn't really think so either," I defended, feeling slightly affronted by her wisdom. "But that's what Aunt Gudrun said she was doing."

"Well, all right," compromised my sister, "you can think it's for the cat, because you're just a little girl."

That night my sister Dode came across the cornfield in the June twilight with her nightgown under her arm. "I'm to sleep at Grandma's," she said, her lost, sad look an anomaly on her freckled, usually optimistic face.

"Goody, we can talk half the night!" I exclaimed, overjoyed at the sudden turn of events. But Dode turned out to be a strangely quiet house guest that night, sharing no special secrets and few words. I fell asleep wondering what got into people sometimes, even those we knew best and loved most.

With morning, Aunt Selma and Bertina came down the path from Uncle Thorvald's, Aunt Selma's broad face exploding into a big grin.

"My goodness!" she exclaimed, pausing by Aunt Gudrun's zinnia bed. "We have the most wonderful news! Guess what, girls!" She looked from Dode's expectant face toward mine. "There's a brand-new baby boy the stork left at Aunt Tina's today! Isn't that wonderful?"

Dally, her eyes dark-shadowed and thoughtful, regarded us dolefully.

Aunt Selma turned toward Dally. "Well, why don't you tell your sisters all about the baby boy?" she prodded. "You know, your sister Dally here was a lot of help around the house."

Dally picked up the corners of her apron, buried her brown head in its folds, and began to sob in explosive bursts. "Maybe everybody else is happy," she cried, "but I think getting born is the worst thing in the world, and I don't feel like being happy right now at all!" Grandma in her mousy, unobtrusive way was now standing beside her.

"Let the poor girl alone," she said. "She was up all night, helping wherever she was needed. Bertina needs a rest." Grandma led her off across the yard into the back door.

In a few weeks when I went calling as usual at Aunt Tina's, she did not always have a dish towel handy. Instead, "Push the baby carriage," she often suggested. "It makes me nervous to hear Sigmund lay there and cry."

3

Harvest   Often in the autumn, shortly before the opening of school, Dode and I would have an invitation to the Weidnar farm to visit the Weidnars' daughter Freda. Her mother always deposited the invitation along with the pound of moist country butter she left upon the drainboard.

"Come early *mit* the morning," she invited, her gold looped earrings dancing from her pierced ears. "Freda, she's planning on it already. The girls can have lunch *mit* puttermilk and blay all day."

Later, left to themselves and the bewildering logic of the adult, Grandma and Aunt Tina construed that "come early *mit* the morning" meant arriving sometime before eleven, when Mrs. Weidnar might suppose that even lazy townsfolk had breakfasted, though not arriving late enough to make her feel we had come just in time for lunch.

So when Aunt Tina had shot the parting gun of approval and Grandma had nodded an amiable farewell with her hands crossed under her white apron, Dode and I set out across the wheat field bordering Grandpa's yard, striking a direct path for the Soo Line tracks that led in the general direction of the Weidnar farm.

From the small rise on which the glistening rails rested, we looked out upon miles of shocked grain, the stubble golden in the clear autumn sky. "You look for trains ahead," suggested Dode. "I'll watch behind." The cool, singing wind was rich with the odor of wheat and sunburned grasses. A green snake slithered along the banked-up railroad bed, slipping into the snarled weeds below us.

"I'm glad I'm not barefoot!" I exclaimed, shuddering. "I couldn't bear to put a foot where the snake's been!"

"Snakes have been everywhere," said Dode philosophically. "You can't let *that* worry you, Mugs."

"Let's turn off the tracks before we reach the bend in the rails where we can see the cemetery," I suggested.

"Okay," agreed Dode. "But can you imagine how Janice's sister Ginger can bear to take her picnic lunch to the cemetery and sit on a gravestone and eat it?"

"Janice won't go with her," I said. "You'd have to be crazy to sit there on top of a lot of dead people and eat your lunch!" I scoffed.

"Ginger's all right," argued Dode. "She just likes the quiet and the trees. Say, are you and Janice friends now?"

"Most of the time," I admitted, walking the left rail and weaving back and forth. "You know what? She's kind of sweet on Normy Rekve, so she has to be friends with us on account of we're at Selma's so much."

We climbed down from the rail bed and slid under the fence marking the south boundary of the Weidnar farm. We saw Freda coming toward us across the fields, waving a continuous welcome and calling to us, her words lost on the wind.

We met her in the middle of a harvested field. "I thought you were *never* coming!" she cried. "Why do you come so late? It makes the day too short!" Entwining her slender tanned arms in ours, she herded us toward the farmhouse, her dark brown eyes snapping with excitement. "Gee, but I like visiting day. Mamma does too. She likes for you to come."

116   Mrs. Weidnar met us at the back door of the big white

farmhouse. "Goodt. You are here," she said, ushering us into the dim kitchen, the curtains drawn to keep out the noon sun. "Git the puttermilk, Freda, and let the girls have a trink." Freda quickly disappeared down the cellar stairway, and we looked about the cool, immaculate kitchen, with its coal range now neatly covered with newspapers, for the cooking in warm months was done outside in the summer kitchen, to avoid warming the house.

Soon Freda's deft, slender hands were pouring us generous glasses of buttermilk, while Mrs. Weidnar inquired warmly about our families. The smaller children, all quiet and well behaved, made a momentary appearance and then ran out to the greater excitement of threshing on their farm. "Vy don't you take the girls to enjoy the barlor, Freda?" inquired her busy mother, starting out for tasks in the summer kitchen.

"Come on," invited Freda, indicating the parlor with a self-conscious little sweep of her arm. In the dining room through which we passed, the big upright piano occupied a prominent place under the stairway. "Come on," encouraged Freda, "we'll go in the parlor and visit for a while, and then maybe you'll play the piano for us later, Dode."

"No, you play," suggested Dode politely.

I took a shiny leather rocker beside a claw-foot table ornately draped with crocheted lace. As I knew they would, my eyes traveled to the wall where a large framed picture hung, holding the casket plate of a departed relative as well as a generous wisp of hair taken from the deceased's head and an inscribed German command to "Rest in Jesus." I
tried not to stare; in fact I earnestly wished not to stare,

lest my dreams the coming night be haunted; but the copperplate and the fading curl of hair always drew my glance to the wall.

Beyond the parlor was the downstairs bedroom, the door open to reveal a neat, shaded room dominated by an intricately carved bedstead, puffy and voluptuous-looking with its feather ticking.

Mrs. Weidnar appeared in the parlor doorway. "Come, girls, come to the zummer gitchen," she invited, her bright blue eyes warm with affection. "The men and the children will eat out in the field mit the cook car. It is just us." Freda ushered us out of the cool, neat rooms to a little house beside the kitchen walk. We stepped down into a room with a cold cement floor and small deep windows. Along the walls hung drying corn, some of it the bright pebbled Indian corn with magenta-red and yellow kernels.

From the little back room where the old range stood came the tantalizing odor of pork and rice rolled into and cooked in cabbage leaves. Freda brought in a steaming bowl of plump little red potatoes, peppered with garden peas and doused with parsley and country butter. Big wedges of fresh bread on a plate beside my place at the table sent up waves of yeasty freshness.

"The bickles! The bickles! Freda, get the bickles out of the stone crock!" ordered her mother, appearing in the doorway with a platter of steaming cabbage bundles, simmering in their rich, meaty juice. "My bickles you say you especially like. I remember, girls," laughed Mrs. Weidnar. "And vy? It's the dill, my own garden dill, and the right spices, dot's vy." She wiped beads of perspiration off her upper lip when she had set the platter down. Freda came in with a dish containing huge chunks of dill pickles. "The corn relish and the domado preserves you must too try," invited her mother, signaling us to start.

"Eat, girls!" echoed Freda, with sudden young pride in her mother's cooking. Platters of dark red sliced tomatoes and ice-green sliced cucumbers were urged upon us. Dode, eying her full plate and remembering her training never to be greedy at the table, said self-consciously, "But you have so much here, Mrs. Weidnar."

"*Ach!*" disparaged our hostess. "Undt vy not? It all comes out of the ground. Alviss there is much ven you feed men upon a farm." She studied our progress. "You afraid to get fat, you girls?" she chided. "Get married and haf a big family, you vork it off, like me," she remarked, indicating her wiry little body. "Maybe you like for it to be more fancy," she suggested.

"Oh no!" we protested. "We love it here!"

"Dot's good. In town your Aunt Tina puts on such a fancy business, it makes me feel shame how plain it is here in the gountry."

"It's wonderful, Mrs. Weidnar," Dode assured her.

"Have some more cabbage bungles," invited Freda's mother, passing me the platter.

"*Bundles*, Mamma, not *bungles!*" stressed her daughter, blushing in painful embarrassment.

"*Ach!*" cried Mrs. Weidnar, throwing up her hands. "They *eat* the same, vodever da vord." Her blue eyes narrowed as she regarded her daughter. "You shame for me, Freda, ven I make da mistakes in front of your friends? *Ach!* Beople understand. You go to school. I did not. You make da fine vords. I make da home."

Freda's dark head was bent over the table.

"The cabbage is wonderful, Mrs. Weidnar," I said.

"Dot's good. The gountry has much good," remarked Mrs. Weidnar, "efen ven it's zimple. Edugation is fine," she continued, glancing at Freda's downcast head, "but ven you haf not edugation, you gif vot you haf. *Mit* my childern, I gif dem a shans like I nefer had." She scraped her chair back from the table. "But come, Freda!" she protested. "Others ve tink of ven ve haf gompany. And you haf baked *such* a fine gake today, *mit* ice gream in the freezer. Da little boy, he turned da crank for it."

"Where is he?" we asked.

"*Ach!* Ven da dresher is out in de fieldt, dey are all dere. Ve used to gook for harvest hands," she continued, "but the cook car, it is better." She set heaped plates of rich ice cream before us. "Alviss there iss enough to do on a farm, mitout cookin' for da dreshers."

Freda came in with a layer cake glistening with chocolate frosting. "Zee?" asked Mrs. Weidnar brightly, her hands on the back of a chair. "Freda, she gooks fine already. Freda's a fine girl, but her feelings get hurt too easy."

"Have some cake," invited Freda, trying to ignore personal allusions from her mother.

"Ven you are dru *mit* the eating," said Mrs. Weidnar, helping herself to a piece of cake, "take the girls out to the field and let dem see the dreshing, yes?"

"Would you like to?" asked Freda politely.

"That's one of the things we came for," said Dode, dimpling happily.

"The thresher's out north of us today," explained Freda,

leading us across the prickly stubble field. In the distance we saw the dark huddle of machinery from which a spume of chaff blew into the air, golden smoke thrown in a graceful arc against the blue prairie sky. A crew of sweating, busy men fed the big throbbing machine with pitchforks of wheat thrown with the effortless grace of habit. Clusters of freckled and openmouthed boys stood watching the men, their arms aching for the taste of combat with the noisy monster of the wheat plains.

The men gave us quick, furtive glances and went on with their work. Mr. Weidnar, his face swarthy above a downward-curling mustache, glanced at us briefly from sharp black eyes, nodded, and went about his work of bossing the men. In the cook car at the end of the field a plump blond woman swung down from the doorway to the rickety step and threw a bucket of water on the field, waved to Freda, and disappeared into the little shanty from whose chimney smoke arose in a straight black line. "Gee! They make seven dollars a day, cookin' for the threshers," said Freda enviously.

The rich, filling odor of wheat dust hung over the field; the thresher throbbed and belched, squeaked and shook. A stooped thin man in dirty overalls poked at the machine with a long-spouted oilcan, drew a grimy sleeve under his nose, and squatted down on the stubble to regard his mechanical charge like a cat listening for a mouse. "Papa says it's a good crop," confided Freda. "Maybe we'll buy a new car."

Wagons piled high with bundles creaked to a stop beside the sweating men. "Let's go," said Freda, tiring of the busy but familiar scene. "Papa doesn't like for me to be out in the field where the threshers are working unless I'm on an errand," she confided between bites of nutty wheat grains we were chewing. "Mom says it's because I'm a bigger girl than I used to be."

Later we all stood in the long drive that sloped down from the farmhouse to the highway. "Do you know what happened to me?" asked Dode. "I haven't told anyone—not even Mugs yet, but my new music teacher that comes from Minot once a week tried to squeeze my waist when I was alone in the living room with him!"

"That old man!" scoffed Freda, but not without a small trace of envy. "How do you stand it?"

"What would Aunt Tina do if *she* knew?" I exclaimed.

"Don't you dare tell her!" warned Dode. "He's a wonderful musician, and maybe that's why he can't help himself."

"I have a secret too," I said. "When I was looking through a box in the attic hole beside our bedroom I found a stack of letters to Aunt Gudrun. I guess I shouldn't have read them—read one, I mean. He said——"

"Who's he?" asked Freda, chewing on a straw.

"Her boy friend in the East," I explained. "He said he was in *prison* longing for her."

The girls stood in shocked silence. "Mugs," said Dode finally, "that doesn't mean what it says. I read a love story from the library and in there a fellow's in love with a beautiful girl—she's redheaded, just like me," she added in an afterthought, "and he tells her living without her is just like living in prison."

"I know," said Freda. "I know just how a woman would feel about a man she loves." Feeling outclassed and subdued, I ran my sandaled foot up and down in the dusty road. "Say, have you seen the new preacher?" asked Freda.

"Why, of course," said Dode; "we've had him over to dinner already."

Mrs. Weidnar came hurrying down the path toward us. "You are leaving so soon?" she asked, a brown paper bundle under her arm and a quart bottle in her hand. "Puttermilk for Grandma," she said, handing me the bottle. "She says her stomach feels bad sometimes. And putter for your Aunt Tina," she said, giving Dode a wrapped parcel.

"We've had a wonderful time," we said. "Thank you for everything."

"Dot's good!" exclaimed our rosy-cheeked hostess. "For Freda it's goodt to have friends. Ve do not always tink togedder. Come again soon."

Freda walked with us to the stubble field where she had met us in the morning. We waved good-by again and again; and when she had disappeared behind a little rise in the land we walked in silence for a while.

A startled meadow lark flew up with a little cry from the long grass beside the railroad right of way. A prairie sunset was marshaling its vivid autumn colors, compounded of wheat dust and smoky haze and stripes of clouds settling into a bank in the west.

The great Northern plains stretching for visible mile after visible mile took on the rounded contours of the curving earth. "We stayed pretty late," said Dode. A mourning dove flew above us in a graceful arc, sang a few trailing notes of twilight requiem, leaving nothing but our crunching steps upon the stubble at our feet.

14

Julekveld   To a Scandinavian, whether he were seven or seventy, the climax of the year was *Julekveld*, or Christmas Eve. Some of the mysticism of Norse mythology, some of Norway's former Catholicism, and a great deal of Lutheranism were all combined in the celebration at home and no one found anything strange in this varied alliance of cultures, nor, perhaps, gave it a passing thought.

"In Norway," remarked Grandma on the early eve of a Christmas, "we used to put food on the doorstep for all the little folk who lived unseen in woods or on mountain crags." She was braiding my long hair and tying the looped ends with green and red plaid ribbons, to match the sash upon my red Christmas dress.

"Who were the little folk, *Bestemor?*"

"Oh, the *niss* and the *troll*, living all about us and rarely seen."

"What did they look like?"

"They were little dwarfs or elves in bright, outlandish costumes, wearing sharp, peaked little caps, getting into all sorts of mischief, like upsetting one's butter churn or causing cream to sour or tripping a soul who was intent upon a serious errand."

"Did you ever see them?"

"*Ja vist,*" said Grandma. "In the midst of our celebrating, if one turned his head quickly enough, he might catch a glimpse of a sharp, curious little face pressed against the window."

"Weren't you frightened?

"*Ja*, but frightened in the same happy way you are when Uncle Thorvald threatens to cut Mons's tail off right behind the ears."

"Did they eat the food you set out for them on Christmas Eve?"

"It was gone next morning," replied Grandma cryptically.

"Maybe the animals in the woods ate it, or a dog or cat."

Grandma put the comb away in the rack above the sink. "How strange it is," she exclaimed, "that you who see so much that isn't there can suddenly explain a mystery many thousand miles away!" Her smile was gentle but mocking. "And have you forgotten," she continued, "that it was you only a few years ago who came running into the house with a tale of a spirit woman who, smiling, floated by you above the edge of the wheat field? How excited you were then, running in with both braids flying!"

"I remember," I admitted seriously. "I called her a mist woman, and I saw her once again in my quiet play."

Grandma took a seat in her rocker by the range. "So you see," she said, "there are mysteries we'll never explain, not upon this earth, at least." She picked up a skein of bright wool for mittens. "Hold out your arms," she said, slipping the skein over my wrists, "that I may wind a new ball of yarn."

"You said that woman who floated by might have been my mother or an angel," I reminded her.

"Who knows what it was you saw? But whatever it was, it sent you running in, perhaps not fear, but great excite-
25 ment."

"Tell me more about Christmas in the old country," I begged, swinging my arms rhythmically to make the yarn slip off more easily.

"You have heard it all, many times," she stressed. "Tonight you may feed Mons a little salmon, for in Norway we always fed our animals an extra ration on *Julekveld*. They, too, in their dumb and silent way share in the glories of a Christ-redeemed world."

"Some people say it's funny to feed your animals before you have fed," I said.

"Oh, is that so?" asked Grandma. "Well, that need not concern us. Animals cannot speak their feelings, and one has but to watch their eyes and see the longing, and sometimes the despair, with which they watch human beings eat while their own stomachs growl in hunger."

I dropped my arms as the last wisp of red yarn found its way to her firmly padded ball. "Be cold to the haughty of this world, if you must," she continued; "but to the helpless and the humble and the needy show only a loving and understanding heart. You yourself may need the help of such a heart someday."

"How soon can we go up to Aunt Tina's?" I asked, eying the clock upon the wall.

"Not until supper," she reminded me patiently, for perhaps the tenth time. "They are busy up there with their preparations."

"Will Uncle Sven be at Aunt Tina's too?"

"*Naturligvis*, naturally."

"How does Uncle Sven always know when someone is having a dinner party, even when he's miles away?"

"What do you mean?"

"Well, he always says, 'Party, huh? I came just in time, so much the better; it would have been a shame to miss it.' " Grandma, catching the heavy mimicry in my voice, gave me a look of hurt disapproval.

"One should be glad that a lonely bachelor has homes in which he is always welcome."

"Why doesn't he ever give presents to people at Christmas?"

"You talk as if your tongue has been stung by an asp," said Grandma. "Why don't you go into the living room and stare at the Christmas tree again?" She rose from the rocker, went over to the stove, and pulled open the oven door gently. "They're done," she said, pulling out two brown-crusted loaves of fruit- and cardamon-filled Christmas bread, called *Julekaga*.

"I have looked at the tree," I said. "It looked lonesome. It seems to know we're going to leave it alone in our dark house and celebrate Christmas Eve at Aunt Tina's. I feel sorry for it. It wants to have people all around it, with the candles lit, and packages under it."

But *Bestemor's* mind was mercifully on other subjects. "Fetch your grandpa from the basement," she ordered. "I see Gudrun and Sven coming down the street together."

A half hour later, when we stamped the snow off in Aunt Tina's back porch, the door was thrown open. "*Glade Jul! Glade Jul!*" Aunt Tina and the girls cried all at once. Dode took the packages out of my arms and greeted me with a happy grin. "You ought to see our tree!" she boasted. "I sneaked into the living room when Aunt Tina went over to Selma's for a minute. It's the biggest tree we've ever had!"

"Are there lots of packages?" I asked, hanging my wraps in the hallway below the stairs.

"More than I have ever seen! Selma's and Grandma and Grandpa Rekve's aren't under the tree yet either. Just before it got dark Aunt Tina sent me on an errand to the store, and I know what Grandpa Rekve is giving you!" she sang.

"What is it?" I asked, going into the kitchen.

"You really don't want to know," she said. "I wouldn't tell you, anyway, because last year when we were just children we told each other and it spoiled everything! Remember?"

In Aunt Tina's fragrant kitchen Grandma was bending over the stove. "Your *rømmegrød* looks fine, Christina," she said.

Uncle Thorvald came into the doorway. "*Glade Jul!* Merry Christmas!" he exclaimed. "I hope you have a lot of good food. I'm as hungry as a bear. I never waited on so many people in my life as I did this afternoon in the store. Last-minute shoppers."

"*Det er godt,* that's good," said Grandpa, appearing back of him in the doorway. "It's good when a businessman complains of too many customers."

"Supper is ready," said Aunt Tina, her smooth white skin becomingly flushed from warmth and excitement.

Bertina lighted the two tall wooden candelabra that were always used at Christmastime; and when we sat down to the table in Uncle Thorvald's paneled dining room we could look across the window-lighted sparkling snow to Selma's dining room on the other side of the fir trees, where the Ronald Rekves and Grandma and Grandpa

Rekve were already seated at dinner. I looked up at Uncle Sven, who sat there making trollish faces at me. "Say grace," commanded Uncle, looking up at Dode.

"*Nu skal ve gaa til bors,*" began my sister, but her voice was trembling with an unexploded charge of laughter, as she stumbled through the remaining words.

Grandma prodded me in the waist. "*For skam!*" she reprimanded softly.

"Don't scold the girls, Mother," laughed Aunt Gudrun. "It's Sven again. He's a bigger kid than the girls." Mundy, sitting in his high chair between Aunt Tina and Uncle Thorvald, banged his silver baby spoon joyfully.

Grandma put a tidy little pile of *lutefisk* on my plate. "I want it in my *lefse*," I whispered. "Rolled in my *lefse.*"

When the *lefse* had been passed, I forked the *lutefisk* upon it, sprinkled it generously with melted butter, and rolled it all into a cigarlike shape. The *lefse*, made of potatoes boiled in their skins, had been peeled, mashed, mixed with flour and salt, rolled into thin tortillalike disks, and baked upon the stove. *Lutefisk* was codfish commercially soaked in a lye preparation and quickly boiled in salted water before serving.

Aunt Tina passed other traditional Christmas Eve dishes, saying, "Save room for the *rømmegrød;* you know how filling that is."

When we three girls had cleared the table Aunt Tina brought in the dessert. "This is truly my favorite," said Grandpa.

"Ole likes anything made of cream!" laughed Grandma.

"I'm going to let you sprinkle your own cinnamon on, 129 or maybe you prefer melted butter," said Aunt Tina, bringing in the coffee cups. I dipped my spoon into the *rømmegrød*. The pudding, literally slow-boiled whipping cream with a little flour and milk added, had a rich nutlike flavor and enough caloric energy to have sprinted across town, given legs. Even so, Aunt Tina pressed cookies and Christmas bread and fruitcake upon us and, when we declined, reminded us that once the children had "had their tree" we should eat again. In the meantime, Uncle Thorvald had turned the living-room lights on. And there stood the tree, as Dode had said it would, with its starry tip almost against the ceiling. Candles, set into silvery clamps, pointed heavenward; and loops of cranberries and puffy popcorn swirled in and out of the thick-needled fir branches. The essence of Northern woods filled the room. At its foot lay packages, reaching upward into the branches.

Uncle Thorvald carried his son over to the Christmas tree. "Better get the dishes out of the way," reminded Aunt Tina. "The folks will soon be here." We moved back and forth between dining room and kitchen, pausing often to glance at the glittering tree. Would I forget my recitation, the poem I had memorized in Norwegian as a special concession to Grandma? I helped the girls stack Aunt Christina's white and green china upon the drainboard. Finally Bertina was ready with her soapy water; and Dode and I stood, towels in hand, waiting for the best company goblets, the "buffet silver" and china. As we wiped we chatted endlessly of surprises and mysteriously shaped packages, wondered whether the pre-Christmas threats and admonitions had reaped an honest or a forgiving harvest. Then, suddenly, I felt a handle slip from my fingers; and there upon Aunt Tina's linoleum lay a white china cup shattered into fragments. "Oh . . . oh . . ." I moaned.

"Can't you girls be more careful?" called Aunt Tina, soon surveying the wreckage from the dining-room doorway. She looked at my stricken face.

Grandma stood beside her. "You did the same thing here last Christmas!" she said.

"I know she didn't mean to," argued Aunt Tina. "It's the excitement of Christmas Eve."

"You run along, Mugs," said Bertina, picking up the rest of the fragments. "Dode and I'll finish." She clasped my shaking shoulders. "Aunt Tina'll order another one from the store to replace it."

"If you cry over a broken cup," said Dode wisely, "you'll spoil our Christmas. You wouldn't want to do that!"

From the front hall came the cries of "Merry Christmas! *Glade Jul!*" A blast of cold air blew through the warm, cigar-filled rooms. Solveig, Signe, and their brother Norman all rushed in, followed by the merry-faced Aunt Selma, Ronald, Grandpa and Grandma Rekve. Packages were again stacked under the tree, where they rose tier on tier.

Aunt Tina plugged in the two amber-colored electric candles on the piano; Uncle Thorvald started to light the candles on the Christmas tree, checking each one carefully to make sure it was not close to tinsel or overhanging bough. We children sat on footstools, hassock, or on the floor, as close to the tree as possible. "Turn out all the lights," said Uncle, and the tree came alive with a mass of flickering candles, lights wavering and dancing with each draft in the room.

131   "Aren't you children glad you aren't Yankee kids?"

laughed Aunt Gudrun. "They have to wait until Christmas morning."

"*Ja*, but we are," said Norman, shaking his pugnacious face seriously. "We're all Americans." He leaned his dark curly head upon upraised palms and stared soberly at the tree.

"Let's have the children's program," said Selma, "before they get too tired." She regarded us with curiosity. "Well, who's first?"

Bertina, her shiny brown hair pinned in looped coils about her head, rose from the floor where she had been sitting with the younger children. "I have the program," she said quietly, "and we're ready to begin." She glanced at the paper in her hands. "The first number on our family program tonight is a recitation by Signe Rekve."

Three-year-old Signe, pushed from the rear by her mother, toddled up to the tree, bent to examine a candle at close range, reared backward, and began to clap her hands. "Your piece, say your piece," prompted her mother.

"Three wise men came . . ." began her sister Solveig in a loud whisper.

"From far away where baby Jesus lay," finished Signe, making a dash for her mother's arms.

Bertina stood before the tree again, waiting a few moments for the indulgent laughter to subside. "Norman will sing 'Joy to the World.' "

Norman, a plump, mischievous-looking eight-year-old, planted his feet far apart, signaled to my sister Dode to give him the right key, and sang several verses of the hymn in a clear, true, boyish soprano. When he had finished he
gave a nonchalant little bow, kicked Solveig surreptitiously

in the back, gave my hair a sharp little yank, and sat down on the floor again.

"Margarethe will now recite *Her kommer dine arme Smaa*—in Norwegian," she added redundantly. My heart hammering against my woolen underwear, I got up in front of the tree and began to survey the family group with bravery; but ended by looking at Grandma, who sat motionless in a small rocker in the dining-room archway, ready to prompt me at the slightest pause. The words came out in spite of me; and when I was through, Grandma commenced to rock again.

"Solveig has a recitation," announced Bertina. Solveig got to her feet and stood before the group, regarding us calmly with huge brown eyes, dark curls falling to her shoulders. Why didn't I pause like that? I thought enviously. Grandma and Grandpa Rekve leaned forward in their chairs to catch her words. "I am going to recite *O Tannenbaum!* in English," said Solveig, turning her cherubic profile toward the flickering tree and pointing toward it with a gracefully cupped hand.

"Don't stand too close," whispered her mother. Solveig took a graceful step forward and recited her memory work without a slip. When she finished, her performance was rewarded with murmurs of approval.

"Now," said Dally, rising once more, "Emily will play some Christmas carols, with variations." Dode, seated at the piano, brushed her hands together, looked down at the pedals, and began to play her medley. When she finished, Bertina rose again. "This ends our program."

"But it is so little," protested Grandma with her deep piety. "Certainly we can spend a few more minutes on

Christmas Eve commemorating the birth of the Christ child." There was an embarrassed little silence, and Selma said, "Why don't we all sing carols together?" Aunt Gudrun sat down at the piano, and all joined in singing except Grandpa, who had no musical pretensions. He sat gazing at the tree as though daring it to burst into flame, having rescued the tree and the church from fire only the year before. Grandma returned to her rocker. Was she thinking of *niss* and *trolls*, I wondered, or of tens upon tens of remembered Christmases?

During a lull in the singing Aunt Tina proposed that the packages be opened. "The kitchen is full of food waiting to be eaten," she reminded us.

"Let me be Santa Claus!" Norman begged.

Grandpa Rekve bent down to pat his grandson's sturdy shoulders. "Suppose I read the labels," he suggested, "and you deliver the parcels."

A few minutes later, sitting in a welter of ribbons and papers and boxes, I called across the room, "Dode, look! Grandma and Grandpa Rekve gave me a red broom!"

"I knew they were going to, remember?"

Solveig looked up from the wrappings and boxes about her.

"Where's my broom?" she asked, her eyes dark-shadowed and hollow with nervous excitement.

"Hush!" silenced her mother. "Look at all the pretty things Grandma and Grandpa Rekve gave you!"

"But I want a broom too. The girls got a broom," insisted Solveig.

"Well," comforted Uncle Thorvald, "there still might be one back of tree. Not all the packages are opened."

136   Solveig jumped to her feet, dancing from the front of

the tree to the back, circling back and forth. Grandpa Rekve shook his head at Selma.

"There's no broom *here!*" wailed Solveig. "Not a single broom left, and I wanted a broom so badly! The girls got a broom." She threw her head into her arms and wept with nervous, convulsive sobs.

Grandma rose quietly from her rocker. "Magrit!" she said, coming over to the place where I sat holding my red-handled broom. "You must give Solveig your broom," she whispered.

"It's mine," I said. "Oh, *Bestemor!* I can't."

"There will be other brooms," she said, disengaging my fingers from the handle. "Now give it to Solveig."

I got up to my feet and went over to where Solveig stood in front of the tree. "You may have my broom. Grandma says so."

Solveig took the broom into her hands. "You made a mistake, didn't you, Grandpa?" she intoned. She whirled and faced in the other direction. "Didn't you make a mistake, Grandma? This red broom was mine all the time!"

"If Margaret will come to the store," said Grandpa Rekve, avoiding any direct admission on the subject, "we'll have a nice, brand-new broom waiting for her."

I sank down on the floor beside Gudrun's chair, as Grandma returned to her rocker. How should I ever bring up the subject of brooms to Grandpa Rekve when I went to the store? Suppose he forgot his promise, as grownups often did! Even Aunt Gudrun had a anything-to-get-rid-of-you promise as well as a this-time-I-mean-it promise. You couldn't walk up to someone and ask him for a present! Tears obscured my vision.

I felt Aunt Gudrun's hand upon my shoulder. "Do you

really like the doll I gave you?" she asked brightly. Then she whispered, "Don't feel bad. Your grandma always likes to be nice to in-laws."

"But the broom is really mine," I said, "even if Solveig is dancing all around the room with it."

In the dining room Bertina was relighting the candelabra. There was cardamon bread inviting us with its light, fugitive fragrance. There were stacks of lefse, plates of fancy cookies, Aunt Tina's molasses-colored fruitcake, fattigman (the "poor man's" cooky of Norway, richly made of eggs, cream, and flour).

"I couldn't eat a bite!" declared Aunt Gudrun, who then picked up a plate and began to place cookies, lefse, and Christmas bread upon it.

"I'm a better eater than a liar," said Uncle Sven, coming up behind her and giving her a sly little pinch. We children hovered about the fringes of the group, speculating upon our choices once our turn came. Signe, a doll clutched to her chubby breast, lay asleep on an end of the sofa, her third Christmas Eve consummated and a memory in her subconscious only. Sigmund was asleep in his crib in the bedroom beyond.

When our plates were filled, we children sat in a small semicircle on the floor before the Christmas tree, comparing notes on gifts, speculating about the coming evening, when we should all be in a Christmas program at the church.

"I'm an angel," said Solveig, flinging brown curls away from her face with a graceful toss of her head. "What are you going to be, Mugs?"

"I'm one of the three kings," I said.

Silver clattered upon plates; the china cups—minus one—were filled and refilled with coffee; the men teased Aunt Gudrun, and Uncle Sven teased the women. I leaned against the upholstered arm of a nearby chair.

"I can tell it's time for the children to be in bed!" laughed Selma. "Mugs is growing paler and paler. That's a sure sign."

"You go on home with Grandma," said Aunt Gudrun, setting her coffee cup on the dining-room table. "We're going on to make some Christmas Eve calls."

"Can't she stay here tonight?" begged Dode.

"Do you want to?" asked Grandma.

"No, I'm going with Grandma," I said.

Later, when my grandparents and I were walking home across the firm, high snowbanks that now separated our houses, I turned to Grandma and asked, "Why was it being nice to the Rekves for me to give my broom to Sol-veig?"

The snow squeaked under our footsteps as Grandma searched for a suitable reply. The frosty stars glistened with rapier sharpness. To the north, beyond the bare-limbed willow grove, the aurora borealis crackled and hissed in the silent night, while a flame of northern lights traveled across the horizon and disappeared. "You have truly given," she said, "when to give was to lose."

5

Neighbors   The house across our grassy lane was in my earliest memory occupied by an aged English couple. Mr.
Appleby, with a white patriarchal beard reaching down

upon his rumpled work shirt, sat outside in an ancient rocker and nodded in the summer sun. His short and stubby wrinkled wife worked in her garden and orchard as though the last trump were about to sound and her harvest of apples, plums, and vegetables must be in by nightfall.

When I rose early in the morning with nothing better to do than awaken a household which cherished sleep as much as I was willing to waste it, I looked out my upstairs bedroom window to see the old woman hoeing at weeds born only that night, coaxing vines up a peeling trellis with the patience only a horticulturist knows, and bracing the gnarled and tired limbs of fruit trees long maltreated by Dakota winds.

Dressing quietly so as not to awaken Aunt Gudrun, I slipped out the back door to the bracing freshness of an early prairie morning. Mrs. Appleby did not always greet morning with the same hearty freshness as her plants. If she noticed my soft approach and said, "Hello, child. Up so early?" I followed her about for a while. If she merely nodded and went about her work as though I had been only a morning shadow upon her lawn, I went back to our own yard and played among the rustling willows until I heard Grandma rattle the grate of the old range.

On the mornings when Mrs. Appleby spoke—and indeed at times she seemed to welcome a repository ear for her mutterings—I was glad to play at her back door, pet the shaggy old collie, and speculate about the sugared vinegar bottle which hung from a looped cord beside the screen door—and which, she told me, caught no end of flies.

Sometimes she let me trail her into the house, where I

was overwhelmed by the amount of kitchen work that always remained undone: dishes scattered on a red-checked oilcloth, with veins of food drying on their rims, jars of jam and pickles standing open upon cupboards, circles of stain at various levels marking their ages like tree rings upon a felled pine. It was certainly true, as the preachers often pointed out on Sunday, that no man could serve two masters; and hers was the outdoors, where weeds and worms and drouth contended for victory.

When I sat upon one of her brown chairs, my fingers tracing the pattern of the checks upon the blood-red oil-cloth, she paused long enough in her stirrings around the dim kitchen to hand me an aging cooky or a dry doughnut.

"Well," she remarked, emerging from one of the ante-rooms surrounding the kitchen and parting the red calico curtains at the door, "guess I'll go to town this morning."

"That's a pretty dress you have on, Mrs. Appleby," I admired, indicating a pebble-printed ecru wash dress on which two bright red roses swayed and swirled over bosom and stomach as she walked.

"That's nice, child. Glad you like it," she replied in the absent-minded manner of adults who have neighbors' children visited upon them during busy hours.

"I don't know why Grandma doesn't sew red roses on her dresses!" I exclaimed.

"Probably never thought to," she said, pinning up the scolding locks escaping to her collar. "I'm a mite more savin' than lots of folks, too," she said.

"Grandma just darns her holes," I confided, "until there's no room to darn any more and then she puts the dress into the rag bag."

"I expect she does," the old woman remarked. "But as for me, I like to appliqué a rose over a hole. But then maybe I'm a mite artistic. And with the old rose quilt ruint, might as well use them pretty roses for something— shame to let them go to waste. That quilt was right pretty, and the roses are big enough to cover a heap of a hole."

"Grandma doesn't have any vinegar bottle at her back door, either," I remarked.

"Well now," soothed the old lady, waddling past my chair, "there's no reason she shouldn't. Vinegar's cheap, and if I say so myself, sugar's cheap at your house too, judgin' from the amount of bakin' and eatin' that goes on all the time. But run along now, dear. This is goin'ta be a busy day." She began to shoo me toward the door.

"Thanks for the cookies," I said, hopping down the wooden stoop. But Mrs. Appleby's replies were lost in a bubbling of soap and water as she bent down to wash her face in the basin at the back door. On the seat of her dress, at the points of hardest wear, bloomed two other roses, which I paused to admire for a fleeting moment, and then I scuttled through the bushes that fringed her yard and ran across the lane to Grandma and breakfast.

One day the Applebys were gone, he in death, she to live with relatives, and perhaps to scratch their neglected gardens to life. Into the white frame house across the lane a new family moved their worldly accumulations as well as the noisy fruits of their marriage: three boys and a girl.

Grandma, whose life was an open book behind a closed door, remarked, "Now don't start running over there to make a nuisance of yourself. The closest neighbors must often live the farthest apart." On my side of the fence I watched the boys rush out of doors like torrents from a spillway. I watched their sister walk out on bare feet to fetch them back to perform some distasteful task around the yard or in the house. The trees, from which Mrs. Appleby's fruit had hung in unblemished perfection, now groaned and cracked under the onslaughts of predatory boys and a barking dog.

Scooping up dippers of fresh rain water from the big barrel beside the front porch, Grandma shook her neatly combed head with resigned dismay. "*Ja*," she said, "it is as I said it would be. Mrs. Appleby would leave someday, and none would ever know nor care about the damp morning hours she dug in the soil nor remember the long twilights in which she planted seeds."

"But the boys love it!" I argued. "See? They're hoisting ropes for a big swing in the trees by the meadow back of the yard."

"What a boy loves," said Grandma, picking up a pail of rain water in which to wash my hair, "he often destroys." Grandma's glance roved across the lane to the rich green foliage of the neighbor's orchard. "Well, she enjoyed her gardens and her fruit trees while she had them, and, *trovist*, in truth, none can possess more than that."

Then one morning Mrs. Tweiler, the new neighbor, called me over across the road with, "Come on, girlie! I've just baked some doughnuts, and you and Nannie can get acquainted over the kitchen table." Grandma guessed it was all right, but permission this time was not to be taken as license to make myself a nuisance at a neighbor's house.

143 Nannie, the eleven-year-old daughter, smiled and pulled

out a chair for me. The kitchen was smoky with the heavy odor of nutmeg and hot fat. "We bake 'em by the dishpan over here!" laughed Mrs. Tweiler, wiping the moisture off her long fuzzy upper lip. "Sit down, Mugs. Oh yes, I know your name. I've heard your aunt calling you. Excuse the place. We're sort of tearing it apart. Never saw such an accumulation of old bottles and musty clothes!"

She turned over sizzling doughnuts with a long fork. "I'll bet that old woman who lived here never threw away a blessed thing in her whole life! Why, do you know, one wall was papered with old post cards?"

"Yes, I know," I said. "I used to study the pictures. Some were way from England."

"And this red oilcloth wall here," she continued, pointing beyond my back, "well, it just gets up and slaps me in the face every time I look in that direction." She pushed the dishpan of moist warm doughnuts toward me. "Help yourself. Don't be bashful. We raise boys, and they don't eat by the piece. They eat like grasshoppers goin' through a field of grain!" she laughed.

"Wh-what grade will you be in, Mugs?" stuttered Nannie politely.

"Fifth."

"Land sakes!" exclaimed Mrs. Tweiler. "You'll have Fred in your class. Fred's my oldest boy. Now don't let him bother you, with teasing and all that."

"Oh, I don't mind. The boys are always putting my braids in the inkwells," I replied seriously.

The back door slammed. The little five-year-old came in, rubbing dirty fists into his eyes and sobbing convul-

144 sively.

"What's it now?" his mother asked, planting her short plump arms on her ample hips.

"The boys wouldn't let me swing." As he reached for a doughnut, his eyes brightening, Mrs. Tweiler gave his wrist a smart little slap. "So help me, I'll skin you alive! With my own bare hands I'll skin you alive, if you don't learn to wash up before you handle food in my kitchen!"

My eyes flew open with surprise, while I studied my voluble hostess to see how much of this strange threat was literal. But Mrs. Tweiler was back at the range again, flipping over sizzling doughnuts and regarding Nannie and me with a serene, motherly expression. What an exciting family! I thought. So different from the gray house across the lane, where the ticking of the old brown clock upon the kitchen wall was often the loudest noise in the house.

"I've heard you p-play the p-piano," said Nannie, wiping crumbs from her mouth with stubby, capable fingers.

"I can't play much," I said.

"Now don't belittle yourself," broke in Mrs. Tweiler, patting out the remnants of doughnut batter. "Don't like to see kids belittle themselves any more than I do seein' them overproud. If there's anything wrong with your playin', it ain't the quality, it's the kind," she said, giving my shoulder a gentle pat as she stuck the flour sifter back into the cupboard. "Maybe too many hymns over there, and not enough music with life in it. Nannie," she said, straightening up with a long tired sigh, "take your company into the parlor and play your new piece for her. 'I'm Forever Blowing Bubbles,' it is."

Nannie led me through the dining room, now bright with fresh calcimine instead of the former tenants' lifetime collection of post cards. In the living room Nannie sat down self-consciously on the piano stool, placed her stubby fingers upon the keyboard, depressed the pedal, and was off in a burst of noisy jazz. From around the corner came a low twittering, followed by nasal meows and a glimpse of the two older boys' crumb-covered faces. "Don't pay no attention to them!" called Nannie without losing a beat of her rhythm. "They're just boys," she called over her shoulder, "and we've got too many of them around here, anyway."

Mrs. Tweiler, bearing a cup of coffee in one hand and several doughnuts in the other, shooed the boys off, threatening them with decapitation if they helped themselves to another doughnut, and settled down in a rocker by the window, tapping her short plump foot in time with the loud music.

"When you finish that, Nannie," she suggested, "let's have 'A Little Gray Home in the West.'"

"What do you like besides playing the piano?" asked Mrs. Tweiler.

"Oh, I like to draw," I said. "But I think I like composition the best."

"Maybe you're goin' to be a writer," suggested Mrs. Tweiler.

"Well, I am writing a story about some girls who left their parents' farm to attend high school in town," I said, warming up to my hostess more than ever.

"Wonderful!" shouted Mrs. Tweiler above her daughter's music. "What your grandma think about you writing?" Mrs. Tweiler glanced across the road to the steep-pitched roof of our house. "Your grandma says she reads mostly religious books herself. I offered her some magazines one day."

"Well, nobody's seen my book," I said. "I hide it under the stairway. There's a little closet underneath, and Grandma's too stiff to clean it out—says she can't get down to the shelves," I confided.

"Now that's all right," laughed Mrs. Tweiler. "Every growing girl's entitled to her secrets. I never bother Nannie's things." She motioned for me to pull up a chair beside her. "Now I'll tell you something, dear," she confided. "I write too. True stories. For Bernarr Macfadden. Have you ever seen the magazine? No, I expect you haven't!" she laughed, regarding my scrubbed and innocent face. "Well, there isn't anything in God's green world I'd rather do," she said animatedly. "Absolutely nothin'. But between kids and work and not too much edgacation, I expect I'll just have to keep on tryin'." She wiped the mist from her eyes. "The truth is, I said I write for *True Story Magazine*. I do. That's the truth; but they don't know it yet, for I've never sold a story since I started." She rocked back and forth, the empty coffee cup on her lap, as she stared dreamily at the wall on which one of the Rekve Store calendars had a prominent billing.

The piano had suddenly grown silent, while Nannie sat studying the knuckles of her hands.

"You play nice, Nannie," I said. "Mrs. Tweiler, I have to go," I began. "Grandma says I musn't stay too long."

Mrs. Tweiler put the coffee cup on the floor. "Yes, Nannie's doin' all right," she said. "Bless your grandma, but you tell her we love to have you come. And while
my kids will never come runnin' in and out of your

orderly house, you come over any time and stay as long as you want to. Nannie needs a friend, and it won't hurt my boys none to have an extra girl around. Might sort of quiet 'em down, if that isn't expecting too much."

I thanked her for the doughnuts and the pleasant afternoon. "Now don't tell folks around town that I write stories," she said. "I keep it a secret, especially since my Harry works in the post office and no one needs to know what goes out or comes back. They think you're a bit peculiar if you aim to do something they can't."

Nannie and she stood together in the doorway. "Now when you get ready for some stories that'll help answer a lot of questions goin' around in your mind someday, I'll sneak a magazine or two to you. It won't do you no harm to learn a thing or two."

"Thanks, Mrs. Tweiler," I said, feeling a glow of pride not unmixed with a trace of guilt.

"Don't thank me, child. I just feel it won't hurt you a bit to read what happens to girls when they grow up. Especially because I think you're going to have a hard time finding out such things, living with a quiet old lady like your grandma and a redheaded aunt that ain't never married." Mrs. Tweiler's words trailed off into a big smile. Nannie waved her hand.

In our kitchen Grandma was opening a can of fishballs. "Did you have a good time?" she asked.

"*Ja vist*," I assured her, not meeting her eyes. I knew how dismayed Grandma would be if she were to discover that I was already planning on a very secret life, its literature to be stored almost under Grandma's feet as she
148 ascended and descended the stairway.

6

Mundy and the Cat   Fluffy, the new cat, had little of Monsey's dignity. "Where do cats go when they die?" I asked Grandma as we sat watching the new gray angora wind himself about a ball of stray yarn. "Where is Monsey now?"

"There's no need to reflect upon his death," answered Grandma. "Cats have no souls."

I poked my finger around the rung of the chair and instantly felt the sharp, moist bite of tiny teeth.

"You said you always fed your animals before you ate, because you couldn't stand to see the beggary in their eyes," I argued. "You said the very heart of a hungry dog or cat shines through his eyes."

"Heart they have," said Grandma with equal stubbornness, "but I said nothing about their souls." Grandma wove the darning needle in and out of the woolen stockings.

"If he knew right from wrong, like knowing he couldn't jump on the table or steal food, he must have had a conscience; and you once said a conscience is the beacon light of our souls."

"You have a new cat," said Grandma, pulling her skirt away from the claws of the playful kitten. "The new kitten was to erase the pain of Monsey's going."

Even Grandpa grew to like the new cat. Accustomed to Monsey's sit-by-the-fire dignity, we were much entertained by Fluffy's sense of adventure. He tripped all over his large paws following Grandma into the pantry with the

149

comic dignity of an unwelcome helper. He sneaked up after us on velvet feet as Grandma and I climbed the stairs to my bedroom, hiding in the closet until the prayers were over and the lights turned out. When the room had become a deep cavern of living darkness, there was a sudden pounce upon the quilt under my chin, and sharp exploring paws struck at my nose. Sometimes he grew so bold downstairs he pounced upon Grandpa's *Skandinaven* to land squarely upon Grandpa's shaking knees. Grandpa, looking pleased for a moment, glanced up to see the amused faces of the womenfolk. "*Den katten!*" he exclaimed, brushing him quickly off his lap. "That cat! I have never had any use for cats!" he extemporized, settling the newspaper quickly before his face again, but not soon enough to conceal the grin of pleased amusement turning up the corners of his mouth below his neat gray mustache.

When school was dismissed afternoons, I raced home across town to play with the new kitten. If the weather was unpleasant we raced up and down the stairway and through the rooms; on pleasant days we scuttled in and out of the tree trunks, with Fluffy darting up the heavy cottonwoods with the agility of a squirrel.

There was only one fly in the cream cup of my full contentment—the afternoons Aunt Tina came down to drink a cup of coffee with Grandma, and Mundy chased the scampering kitten about the rooms. His arms extended to embrace him, Mundy pursued the kitten up and down the stairway, through the downstairs rooms, and, when he caught him, squeezed him around the middle, until he 150 looked like a tube blown up at either end. The kitten's mews grew fainter and fainter. I dashed to take him from the toddler's arms.

"What's the matter now? Aren't you two children getting along?" demanded Aunt Tina, calling from the other room.

"For skam!" reprimanded Grandma. "Don't tease Mundy. Let him have what he wants."

"He wants to squeeze Fluffy until he can't breathe. He hurts his stomach."

The rescued kitten in my arms, we stood defiantly in the doorway. "I've never seen a cat who couldn't take care of himself!" laughed Aunt Tina.

When the little coffee party was over and Aunt Tina and Mundy were walking across the field toward home, I asked, "Why doesn't Aunt Tina scold Mundy when he hurts my cat?"

"Doesn't she?" replied Grandma with the exasperating blankness she always assumed when a controversial family question was the issue.

"She usually looks the other way."

"He's just a little boy," said Grandma, beginning to clear the coffee cups, saucers, and plates from the round table, and setting the teakettle on to boil for dinner.

Sometimes it wasn't only Fluffy who suffered from the afternoon visits of a mischievous little boy. Fascinated with Grandpa's carpenter bench and the long curls of wood that drifted down from the plane, Mundy liked nothing better than to visit with Grandpa when he was at work. When the novelty of the carpenter room wore off, Mundy wandered past the furnace and into the coal room, with the bins of lignite and hard coal stacked high against the walls. Once when he and Grandpa were alone in the house Mundy, now able to reach the hook on the basement door, locked Grandpa in and took off across the field for home. How long Grandpa worked before he discovered his imprisonment I'm not sure; but when he did, he had no other alternative but to remove the cellar window or await someone's return. While it was nothing for Grandpa to spend an afternoon at his workbench, it was a different matter when it became compulsory. When I came home from school I found Grandpa, perspiring and disgruntled, halfway out of the cellar window, with the windowpane lying neatly beside him in the grass.

Mundy's exploit became a family tale; and like most children, Mundy was loath to leave the limelight. One May day I returned from school to greet Fluffy waiting for me in the warm sunshine on the back steps. No one was at home, but Grandma had left the usual after-school lunch for me on the kitchen table. When Fluffy and I went out into the green spring afternoon to play under the cottonwoods, I heard a loud banging from the direction of the chicken house. But when Fluffy and I investigated we discovered that the sounds originated from the little outhouse nestling picturesquely under the shade of the cottonwoods at the rear of the yard. "I will out! I will out!" yelled Grandpa in his vernacular. I unhooked the door, which had an outside latch to keep the persistent prairie wind from revealing the interior to passers-by. Out strode Grandpa, looking furious and ill-tempered. "That foolish boy!" he exclaimed. "Can't they teach him to leave locks alone!"

Several afternoons later I returned from school to find

Grandma doing up the coffee dishes. "Aunt Tina and Mundy have been here!" I exclaimed, looking at the stacked cups.

"So they have," said Grandma, fetching the singing kettle from the range to scald the dishes.

"Did you put Fluffy away?"

"No," said Grandma, not meeting my eyes as she walked by with the empty kettle. I flung out the back door and began to call the kitten.

Outside the cottonwoods and the willows with their young leaves set up a soughing and clapping that filled the late afternoon air. I searched everywhere, even in the hateful chicken coop with its ammoniac stench of chicken and feathers; but if Fluffy were playing his game of hide-and-seek he had learned to do it with cunning as well as stealth.

The tall grasses along the border of the newly plowed wheat field beside our fence rose and fell in wind-rippled shadows, their whispering sharp and soft in the overtones of creaking branches and rising wind. Where was Fluffy? How could anything young and lighthearted and supple resist the Lorelei invitation of the spring wind to romp and dance before night should close the book of this May day?

I raced through the back entry and into the warm kitchen. "*Bestemor*, I can't find the cat!"

She looked up from the sewing on her lap. "And you never will," she said sadly. "I was looking for the words with which to tell you before you flew out into the wind."

"He is lost?" I asked quickly.

154   "No, dead."

"Mundy do it?"

"*Ja*, Sigmund did it." She stood beside me, stroking my head gently. "He didn't mean to," she said. "He is only a small boy. He squeezed him too hard when he held the cat in his arms."

"But I told you he would do that! I told you! You and Aunt Tina just sat there with your coffee cups and smiled and said, 'He's just a baby.'"

"So we did," admitted Grandma. "I did not know how hard he could squeeze, and I have always sought to keep my peace with everyone, and with family most of all."

Sitting on the settee under the ticking clock, I sobbed away bewilderment and shock. "I almost hate Mundy, and Aunt Tina for not scolding him!" I said.

Grandma set the silverware on either side of the green-and-yellow-bordered plates. "I need not point out the ungodliness of such a remark," she answered with piety. "Nor must you say a word to either of them when you go up there."

"Where is Fluffy now?"

"Your grandpa buried him." Grandma pulled a pan of soda biscuits from the hot oven. "Nor must you plague your grandpa when he comes home. He left because he did not wish to see your grief nor could not bear to tell you, so tenderhearted he is toward you." She smiled. "He even liked the cat, and he has never been one to waste kind words on a cat."

"Where did he bury it?" I asked, washing my face in the basin in the sink, cold rain water slipping through my fingers like cool satin.

55   "What good would that do you, to know?"

"Where did he bury it, *Bestemor?*"

"Along the fence by the cottonwoods," she said.

When summer came I got used to lying in my bed without the cat pulling at the woolen ties upon the quilt and sharing the shadowed loneliness of long summer twilights. What I could not get used to was the fact that nothing had ever been said about the loss of my cat, up in the blue-gray house across the field.

How could Aunt Tina forget that a child needed a soft word of regret even more than a drink of water beyond his reach?

17

"Even When Steeples Are Falling"[1]   The Baptists and the Lutherans worshiped a stone's throw away from each other, and on warm summer days their hymns mingled in a rising disharmony that would have frightened off a less stern God than the One in their theologies.

"We've got a nice young minister in our church," I frequently boasted to Mamie Schimmelfuss, who often waited for me on the corner near her house, her feet planted firmly on a snowbank, her black hair capless and shining with health, even in the zero winds blustering down from the arctic reaches of Canada.

"Well," said Mamie philosophically, matching her steps with mine, "I don't care, Mugs, really I don't. Because if you don't have the one true faith, the kind of preacher you have don't matter one little bit."

[1]From "Built on the Rock the Church Doth Stand," *The Lutheran Hymnary* (Minneapolis, Minnesota: Augsburg Publishing House).

Since Mamie and I shared a friendship born in travail, being easily the poorest arithmetic students in our class, we never allowed our arguments to bear fruit, but plucked them off the vine at the peak of their flowering.

"How do you Baptists know you have the one true faith?" I chided.

"Why, our preacher says so!" scoffed Mamie.

"Maybe our preacher says the same thing about our church!" I teased.

"You'll never convince *me!*" Mamie shifted her books to the other hip. "Anyway, your church is full of sinners," she continued. "We weed ours out. Why, we have a trial for those who fall from grace, like old man Munster, who got roaring drunk last week. If they repent we take them into the fold again. But you Lutherans," she chided, her brown eyes fiery with delight, "you just let 'em keep on coming, black sins or not!"

"We do not!" I shouted, following her down a shoveled sidewalk between walls of hard-packed snow.

"You do too! You do too! Everyone knows how Swedes and Norwegians like to drink. Why, I could name——"

But the school bell began to ring, its clanging thrown to us on gusts of wind, a burst of sudden sound dinning at our ears, then wafted away to return on a final whining note.

"Let's hurry!" Mamie called back. "Someone's sure to have the answer to our arithmetic if we get there soon enough."

At home these days I managed to pique Grandma by asking how I could assume that God was the champion of the Lutheran faith, when I had already discovered that He was not a Norwegian.

"Such questions," disparaged Grandma, "must be inspired by Satan himself, who enjoys planting seeds of doubt in willing minds." She sat down in one of the carved rockers in the living room. "It must be a sign of the times," she bewailed. "Even our Lutheran church here, founded by Norwegians, paid for by Norwegians, and maintained chiefly by Norwegians, must now bear the name 'English Lutheran.'"

Aunt Gudrun settled down upon the settee Grandpa had conveniently combined with the furnace register, so that hot air billowed against legs and warmed cold feet. "Mor," she said, "we'll attract many more worshipers if we do not insist upon being clannish. Why, our new choir has voices which have never sung in church before."

"And never ought to," suggested Grandpa dryly. "*Katta-larm*, cat noises some of those women make. Enough to drive the timid away from God forever!"

"Ole," suggested Grandma, "take care how you criticize the church before the young. They seem to be born breathing doubt these days."

"Well," said Grandpa, who was most expansive and relaxed when discussing anything philosophical, "our new minister is not one who would bid the sun to stand still, nor one day to be as unchanged as the next."

That was right, I thought, doodling along the margin of my arithmetic paper. Reverend Kjelland was nothing like the itinerant clergymen who had preached to us before, older men with the kindly pomposity of the Norwegian Lutheran minister, portly men who rarely showed any dislike toward the delights of the dinner table or spurned worldly comforts. The young Reverend Kjelland, tall, tanned, and self-assured, strode down the church aisle with his great black robe swinging about his feet, and shook the hands of his people in a bold and businesslike way.

"If he only spoke in Norwegian," insisted Grandma, "I could understand all his fine words much better."

"Those you can understand, Guro," said Grandpa, "are strong and good. Better a little well said than a discourse of no consequence."

The new minister called at our house, leaving Grandpa with the promise of some new theological volumes and Grandma with the feeling that, if he talked above her head sometimes, he *did* eat and drink coffee like a Norwegian. Aunt Gudrun, surprisingly, did not have much to say at all but practiced the preludes and postludes on the upright piano in our living room with a new dedication to music, for she was the church organist.

"Too bad you aren't younger," teased Uncle Sven, home for a day's visit. "You could be a preacher's wife."

"I've had my chance at that!" scoffed Aunt Gudrun with a toss of her coronet-braided hair. "No, thank you. I like to speak my mind too well for that."

In the meantime the choir suddenly bloomed with girlish faces of young schoolteachers who had found a church home with the Lutherans. An assortment of unattached women stopped searching for their souls in one church or another and became willing to sit through, if not actually listen to, sermons born in a sixteenth-century religious revolution. Even a running child could read the signs. "Church tramps!" scoffed Grandpa.

"One must not be so critical," said Grandma. "Who can search the soul but God?"

"Why, we even have a Catholic singing in our choir!" exclaimed Grandpa, remembering his wife's prejudice in that direction.

"Well, her voice comes from God," said Grandma.

The new church building was at last a reality, the dream of early pioneers and the fruit of Grandpa Rekve's planning and promotion. It stood two blocks north of the Rekve Store on Main Street, a white-timbered structure with a flight of concrete steps to the foyer under the tower. When the oak doors swung open to the auditorium, there were the picture of Christ in Gethsemane in the middle of the altar and the red plush carpeting around the communion rail and the white altar cloth done in Aunt Gudrun's neat stitching.

On a Saturday afternoon when Aunt Gudrun slipped into the church to practice on the organ, I sat on a bench in the rear and smelled the clean mingling of timber, paint, and varnish. I watched the late sun gild the light oak pews, kindle the flame of Aunt Gudrun's hair, and cast a mellow pearly glow on the face of Christ praying for the sins of the world.

Something holy was in the little church, a quietness and a solitude that clean timber and a small vaulted arch and Aunt Gudrun's forthright playing could not entirely account for. I seemed to hear *Bestemor's* gentle voice singing:

"Built on the rock the church doth stand,
 Even when steeples are falling."

I remembered the times Grandpa talked of the ancient churches of Norway, ornately timbered structures pointing their cross-topped spires above pine and spruce, churches clinging to the steep rocky soil at the edge of deep blue fjords, simple country churches nestled in valleys heavy with blossoming fruit trees.

Child that I was, I sensed the almost primitive faith in the Norwegian people I knew, a faith often shaken by conflicting ideologies and theologies, but a faith as basically simple as wind upon water and the waving spire of a fir tree on a breezy mountainside. Aunt Gudrun and I walked down the aisle of the little church and out into the lavender and pink sunset of a fall evening, down the now quiet Main Street, past the Rekve Store on the corner, down the sidewalks to the gray-blue house in the hollow by the willows.

At the back door Grandma met us with a nervous twitching at her mouth and eyes misted behind her bifocals. "Ole doesn't want it," she said, "but I think we must have the doctor."

"I'll call from Tina's," said Aunt Gudrun quickly. "I knew Father wasn't well!" she cried.

Later that evening Dr. Whitaker knotted a scarf about his throat and put on his overcoat. "Grandpa Henrickson needs an operation," he said. "It's unavoidable and must not be postponed." He spoke in the quiet, conspiratorial way of country doctors. "I'll make hospital arrangements in Minot." He glanced at Aunt Gudrun and Grandma. "Now leave the worrying to me, please."

The next day the church cornerstone was laid with all the pomp and ceremony an occasion of that sort in a little community always inspired. Grandpa insisted that all the family attend, but Grandma sat beside his bed like a figure carved from gnarled wood. After the morning service in the overcrowded church I watched Grandpa Rekve go down the aisle with Grandma Rekve, and the look of triumph and achievement on their faces seemed to say, "Look what planning and perseverance can accomplish!"

Later when they stood outside talking with Aunt Gudrun about Grandpa, who at his carpenter bench in the basement had had little to offer toward the building of the church but the work of his hands, tears filled their eyes, and Grandpa Rekve turned away to blow his nose and wipe away a tear.

That night a German girl from the country came to take over our kitchen, since Grandma would be gone to Minot in the morning with Grandpa. When I left for school the next day Grandpa took my hand and said, "I have been sick often, and as I grow older I shall probably be sick more often than I am well. But you are young and must not stand with tears beside the beds of the old. Run along to school, and be sure my thoughts will go with you."

In school the pages ran blurred before me. At noon when I heard the sudden whistle of the westbound, I could almost see Grandpa's stretcher pulled on the train, so vividly did I picture each moment beside the little yellow depot, whose roof was visible from the upstairs schoolroom.

At noon Aunt Gudrun and I returned to a house smelling of disinfectants and laundry soap. When the dessert came, Ella, the new hired girl, set before us a brown concoction that rose with our spoons like clay from a scoop shovel.

162   "Whatever is this?" cried Aunt Gudrun.

"Choglate pudding," said the stolid blue-eyed newcomer.

"I've never seen one this stiff!" laughed Aunt Gudrun.

"Izz dat zo?" she replied.

"How much starch did you put in?" persisted Gudrun.

"Vot I alvizz put in," said Ella.

"That's strange," said Aunt Gudrun, not liking to push her dish away, hired girls being hard to find on short notice.

Ella brushed aside a curling wisp of light brown hair and sat down at the table with us, staring at her pudding. "Clothes starch it izz. Might have made it stiffer. I dunno. The other starch I could not find." She shrugged her shoulders eloquently.

Aunt Gudrun and I broke into laughter, and it was like sunshine finding its way into a cellar room, the house had been so still and desolate. The brown clock on the wall seemed to repeat with each echoing tick, "*Bestemor, Bestefar.*" The fall day was chilly and overcast.

"There's a special choir practice tonight," said Aunt Gudrun, rising from the table to get back to the courthouse. "I won't be home for supper, as Grandma Rekve is having Anna Norquist and me in for supper. Grandpa Rekve, you know, goes to Minneapolis today on the afternoon train." Aunt Gudrun hugged me affectionately. "You don't mind, do you? I asked Ella to make your favorite spaghetti for supper." She laughed. "There's no clothes starch in that!"

That evening, after a dish of spaghetti and leftovers, Ella suggested that I wipe the dishes for her, since I had sat in school all day. "Me, I vorked and vorked," she said, sighing greatly. I looked at the remnants of spaghetti in Grandma's round vegetable dish, pale tubes swimming in a sea of watery tomato juice, looked up at Ella's square face staring at me across the tablecloth, and decided I could muster no argument against her unanswerable German logic. A cold scudding rain lashed at the pantry window as I wiped the dishes she thrust into the rinsing pan. Ella stared out the dark narrow window and sighed deeply from the bottom of her country-loving heart.

Afterward I settled down to the kitchen table with my schoolbooks, while Ella sat down in Grandma's rocker, staring defiantly at the coal range growling at spurts of rain attacking the long nose of its chimney. "Do you know where babies come from?" she asked, turning to meet my shocked glance.

"I . . . I suppose so," I said uncertainly.

"You za-pose zo!" she exclaimed. "A country girl would not guess at sudge a thing. A country girl would know!" She rocked back and forth as though her menial position in life had now been vindicated. She eyed me shrewdly. "Witt all your books and your studying, I don't think you are zo smart!" She gave me a taunting smile, the corners of her mouth turned upward. "Zee? I know you don't know where babies come from! Isn't that zo?" She waited while the clock at her back chimed in its deep resonant tones seven times. "You are a *dummkopf* if you do not already know why a man marries a woman——" Her voice froze into a startled silence as a sharp slapping sound echoed from the darkened living room.

"*Gott im Himmel!*" she cried, jumping to her feet. "Vot vass dat?"

I got up from the table, my knees trembling. "I think it was a roller curtain," I said weakly. Ella followed me as I went to the living-room doorway and groped for a light switch. "See, that's what it was!" I said, sighing with huge relief as I saw only one green shade lowered to the sill on the other side of the lace panels at the double window.

When I came back to the table Ella was staring at me with a quiet sort of horror. "You know vot dat means? Venn a curtain rolls all up by itself?"

"No, I don't," I said, coaxing Mousy, the new cat, to my lap, and feeling less frightened by a peripatetic shade than by the intense young woman sitting beside the fire.

"Dat means," began Ella pontifically, "dat means that someone in dis house will die. Maybe your grandpa!"

I said nothing but lifted Mousy against my chin and cradled his warm furry body in my arms. The coal in the basement slipped noisily down into the bins; the house shook in the windy fall rain. Suddenly the loud slapping echoed from the living room again, followed by the fading whirr of the settling roller. "Grosser Gott!" yelled Ella. "I do not like it here!" She rose from the rocker as though confronted by a spirit. "Dat's more than I can stand!" she wailed.

Together we went back into the living room to pull down the blind. Across the street I caught a glimpse of the Tweiler house cheerful with lights in every room; and I no longer seemed alone. Still, I wished that Ella had not said that.

The next morning I awakened to a world quiet and

feathery white under the first winter snow. During the

night the cold rain had stopped and snow had fallen upon the iced branches of trees, upon telephone wires, upon roofs, clinging in iridescent sparkles to all the surfaces that yesterday had looked ravaged and worn. "It looks like a sugar world," I said to Aunt Gudrun, who had Grandma's place beside the sink, combing my long braids for school.

There was a sound of running footsteps upon the snowy walk at the back door, the quick beat of feet in the back entry, and when the kitchen door was flung open we looked up at Aunt Tina's excited face, the pale freckles on her fair skin standing out like raindrops pebbling snow.

"We just had a telephone call," she said. "Grandpa Rekve is dead."

"Dead! He can't be!" cried Aunt Gudrun, her brush falling to the sink. "Why, he took the afternoon train to Minneapolis yesterday!"

"Killed by a speeding car," said Aunt Tina, her voice breaking. "Poor Thorvald, he could hardly get the details, he was so shocked."

"How did it happen?" asked Gudrun, slipping into a kitchen chair.

"He and a professor from the theological seminary had just stepped out of the railroad station. A private ambulance returning from a call came speeding down the street without its siren. Grandpa was dragged under its wheels for almost a block——" Aunt Tina began to sob.

"And only yesterday morning," said Aunt Gudrun, "he helped raise Father's stretcher on the train, and when the train started to pull away Grandpa Rekve shook his head and said, 'I know I shall never see Grandpa Henrickson again. Something tells me I shall never see him again. I have said good-by to him forever.'"

During the week a hush fell over Grand Prairie. Upstairs in the comfortable apartment above the store, Grandma Rekve moved about in a state of shock, too stunned even to weep. The little town of Grand Prairie prepared to say farewell to a pioneer who had come to the plains to help found schools and churches and two country stores, besides the big brick building on the corner of Main Street.

In a few days *Bestemor* stepped off the eastbound train from Minot; and when she was back in her familiar kitchen she sighed. "How sad it is for the Rekves now! It is as I have always said, 'We go in peril where'er we go.'" She sat down at the table and poured cream into her coffee cup. "But we have so much to be thankful for, with your grandpa getting stronger every day. Why, he can hardly wait to get home again!"

"And I can hardly wait to see him!" I exclaimed. I said soberly, "But, *Bestemor*, I can't go to Grandpa Rekve's funeral. I can't!"

"We'll see," she said.

But in the pantry a few minutes later I heard Aunt Gudrun say, "Why make her go? She'll brood about it for weeks."

So Grandma let me stay at home while most of Grand Prairie gathered in the new church. I put my new skis on and rode up and down the avenue made by the bare cottonwoods, their lean jagged shadows striated upon the snow. Stores and school were closed, and not a child's voice nor a laugh rang out across the still town.

I was glad, then, that *Bestemor* had made me give Solveig my broom. I knew what she meant when she said it **167** was well to get along with one's own people.

18

The Lake   It was a wonderful winter and spring, with Grandpa home again and growing steadily stronger. In our families, one grandfather was gone, and in our minds the return of the other one was doubly dear. Summer came, with the lilac bushes in Uncle Thorvald's yard swelling into fragrant bloom.

When Aunt Tina remarked early in June, "Isn't Mugs going to the lake with us this year?" Grandma demurred a little, saying that Aunt Tina already had three children to look after; but the argument had little substance, since Bertina was rapidly becoming a young lady, and we girls had been well schooled in the art of making ourselves useful, at home or upon visits.

"Well," conceded Grandma finally, "you may go along again if you remember to review your Catechism and the Explanation."

The night before we set out in Uncle's big seven-passenger Buick, it was hard to imagine who was more excited: Mundy's fox terrier, Chum, or I. Although Aunt Tina had suggested I sleep up at their house that night, I wanted to be near Aunt Gudrun; for who knew what might occur when I was gone? I might even return to find myself evicted from her bed forever. Chum quieted his feeling of insecurity by sleeping under the car when he was not sneaking into it, and panting with colossal excitement every time the car door was opened to stow away supplies and baggage.

168   The chilly morning soon came, with the rolling prairies

luminous in the fading gray light preceding sunrise. After a breakfast in which Grandma urged victuals upon me as if we were leaving on a foodless voyage, I slipped upstairs to say good-by to Gudrun, who planted a sleepy kiss upon my cheek and told me to run along and have a happy summer; but I stood there buzzing with the mosquito of verbal confusion. How did one tell a pretty young aunt not to get married during one's absence and leave a house desolate with the loss of her laughter and badinage? "Run along, dear," she finally said, propping herself up on an elbow, her heavy red braids falling to the snowy sheets. "Don't worry about a thing, and have a good time."

Downstairs Grandpa waited for me with my suitcase in one hand. Together we walked across the potato field and through the rows of growing corn, saying little but sensing already the emptiness that came with parting. Later Grandma followed our steps across the field and through the iron gate at the back of Uncle Thorvald's yard, her long black skirt trailing the dewy grass, her hair neatly combed.

Aunt Tina, her pleasant face by now looking severe from the ardors of packing the car and closing the house, frightened me a little; and in a panic of parting and fear, I stood between my grandparents, holding on tightly to their bony hands, and measured in a tumble of thoughts the glory of a summer at the lake against the pleasant security of life at home.

Uncle Thorvald emerged from the cluster of flowering bushes at the back door, keys jingling in his hand, and said, "All right, all right. Get in, all of you! The sun will be up before we start!"

"Come on, Mugs!" called the girls as they opened the back door of the touring car. Chum made a flying leap into the back seat, and we followed. Uncle backed the Buick out of the yard, with Grandma and Grandpa waving gently and calling, "Farvel! Farvel!"

Aunt Tina settled the wriggling Mundy in the seat beside her and, turning to Uncle Thorvald, worried, "I hope we haven't forgotten anything this time."

Once out of Grand Prairie, we saw the rich black loam of the Dakota prairies stretch from horizon to horizon, the monotony broken by clumps of trees planted as windbreaks to shelter farm buildings from the predatory northwest wind. Utility, economy, and necessity gave a pattern to all the farms we passed: boxlike white-painted farmhouses, flanked on either side by red barns and small utility buildings.

As children will, we played games to while away the hours. "The people in this farm," laughed Dode, "are Germans, because Uncle says if the barn is much, much bigger than the house, the man's the boss, and German men always boss their wives."

"I am thinking of something visible," said Bertina dreamily, "something starting with *j* and belonging to the mineral and vegetable kingdom."

"Jelly," I guessed. "Some of Aunt Tina's jelly in the lunch basket!"

"There's no mineral in jelly!" scoffed Dode.

"There's paraffin on top," I contested hotly, "and that's mineral."

"But paraffin doesn't start with *j*."

170   "What's going on back there? Anybody feel like walk-

ing?" called Uncle Thorvald, the smell of his pipe tobacco wafting back to us.

"No fighting!" called Aunt Tina, holding onto Mundy by the seat of his rompers.

"We're not fighting, Auntie," said Dode. "We're playing a guessing game." Chum, excited by all the voices, leaped from his pallet on the floor and washed our faces with his rasping, sandpaper tongue.

"I can see it now," continued Bertina in her soft-spoken pedagogical manner.

"The James River!" exclaimed Dode.

"Yes," agreed Bertina. "The water is mineral but floats a vegetable content."

From the central plains of Dakota we were now descending to the Red River Valley, down a chain of softly rounded hills, the little draws between them gracefully feathered by tops of trees. In Valley City we drew up to a well-shaded picnic ground beside the river flowing quietly between grassy banks. Aunt Tina gave us all errands: fetch the newspapers to lay upon the stone tables, exercise Mundy and the dog, find the tablecloth, get the dishes, bring the potato salad—oh yes, the salad was in the basket if we'd only take the time to look.

Uncle Thorvald walked slowly around the car. "No flats!" he exclaimed with congratulatory pride, since traveling in the early twenties was rarely ever completed without a flat tire or two. Aunt Tina's fresh graham bread, thick slices of roast beef, potato salad, homemade dills, fruit, and a variety of cookies comprised our lunch, while the grownups poured themselves cups of fragrant hot coffee

from a quart thermos bottle.

When we were back in the car we could scarcely wait to cross the Red River, flowing quietly between grassy shaded banks on its long journey northward to the Hudson Bay; for then we were in Minnesota. And always I came to Minnesota with love and left with regret. If every human being has his climate somewhere upon the face of this revolving earth, mine was in the region of trees, hills, and water; and I knew it as surely as a wanderer returning home. We watched for the first surprising sight of a lake coming into view around the bend of a hill, its water blue and clear in the bright June sky, trees and thickets marching down to sandy shores. We watched for tiger lilies in some swampy place between grassy hills, their tawny freckled heads nodding in the breeze. We watched for cattails bordering a little creek whose rumbling wooden bridge we crossed. It didn't matter now if Mundy's fox terrier panted with anticipation and crawled all over us to sniff at the smells of water, strange fields, and scented woods; nor did it matter if Mundy, long ago tired of the front seat, crawled all over us and whined away his increasing boredom and discontent. From the tops of hills we were nearly always able to see some lake lying serene and cupped in the curved wooded lap of the land.

"Who is going to see our lake first?" the girls teased, while I sat admiring the easy way in which my sisters spoke of their lake, yet knowing even then that eyes which caressed God's great earth with a loving heart might possess it within the span of memory.

Suddenly there it was, lying far below us, lapping against rounded hills, shadowy beside the timber that stretched down to the shore, curving gracefully around a wooded island and a long sand bar that formed a peaceful cove. A country road full of sharp angles and steep grades circled us around a portion of the lake; and soon we were at the big gate into the woods. Dode opened the car door as Uncle slid to a stop; with a wide grin on her freckled face, she held the sagging gate open as the Buick rattled over the cattle guard.

Presently we were climbing into the shadowy woods, with Uncle shifting the long car into low and rocking back and forth with excitement as he willed the motor to pull. Thickets of hazelnut bushes, overhanging boughs, and large ferns trailing delicate green leaves made passing thrusts at the wheel spokes. When Uncle swung the car sharply to descend a treacherously steep and curved road, we caught a glimpse of the cove, shining green and cool below us. The car purred down a long lane between overhanging boughs of oak, ash, elm, and maple, at the end of which stood the red-brown cottage. In back of it towered a steep hill densely covered with climbing, straight-limbed trees; in front of it lay a little shelf of grassy land that dropped sharply to the clean white sand of a small beach.

As Uncle braked the car the children in the Thorvalson cottage we had passed spilled out of their doors with shrieks of delight. Their father, Uncle's banker and old friend from Grand Prairie, waddled out on tender bare feet to give Uncle the latest reports on fishing and weather. While Aunt Tina unlocked the back door of the cottage, we children ran down to the pier and stared out across almost a mile of sparkling, tumultuous water, with the waves frothing under the pier and shaking the wooden piling.

"Let's help get the cottage cleaned up in a hurry so we can go swimming," suggested Dode. Mattresses were pulled down from taut wires on which they had been hung to keep mice away; the boat and the outboard motor had been dragged out of the cottage to the pier. There were cupboards to wash out with naphtha soap and cleansers, floors to be swept and mopped, and rugs to be laid. At dusk, when we had refreshed ourselves with a swim in cold water, the long trestle table at the Thorvalsons' invited us, with a huge platter of sunfish, crappie, and bass fried to a crisp, crumbly brown. Back at the cottage, Uncle ordered us all to bed early. "Fishing in the morning," he said.

But we should have remembered what Uncle meant by "morning." We were awakened in the semidark to hear Uncle knocking at the thin pine partition that separated the cottage bedrooms. "Up, you lazy girls!" he ordered. "There's nothing like a brisk swim to get in the spirit of the lake!" I sat up and studied Dode gravely.

"Does he mean it?" I whispered.

"Sure," she said. "He wants minnows for bait, and we have to get 'em." Dode shivered her way into a nondescript bathing suit.

In the long living room Uncle looked up from his breakfast. "Now that's more like it," he smiled, his grin hammocked from ear to ear. "Always have an early swim, and breakfast tastes twice as good." Uncle himself sat all bundled up in a heavy brown sweater, with a leather jacket swung across the back of his chair.

"Better run along," suggested Aunt Tina, coming from the kitchen dressed in old clothes for her morning of fishing. "The net is waiting on the shore, Uncle says."

Dode and I tiptoed on tender pale feet to the little sandy beach and the water green and glassy in the quiet morning. She looked back over her shoulder at me. "Let's get it over with," she suggested, handing me a heavy wooden pole on one end of which the seine was fastened. We stuck exploring feet into the water. "The best way," continued Dode, speaking from long experience, "is to wade bravely in and, when it gets deep enough, get wet all over suddenly."

Dragging the long net between us, we plunged into the cold water, shivered, and waded out to a point where the water reached above our waists. "Now duck," said Dode, squatting until the water reached up to her head. I followed.

"What I can't understand is why our suits don't get full of minnows when we go in swimming. If they're all around and can get in the net, why don't we swallow them when we float with our heads down in the water?"

"I'm sorry," said Dode politely, "but we can't take time for a discussion here. The folks are coming down to the beach now." She jerked the net to pull it taut. "All right, let's seine in." We tugged against the weight of the water. When we got to the shore, they were waiting, Aunt Tina and Uncle, Bertina, and the Thorvalsons, dressed in the nondescript castoffs they always wore to go fishing, looking like derelicts who had been cast upon shore.

"Well, well!" beamed Uncle. "Let's see what we've got!" Bait buckets in hand, he and Mr. Thorvalson squatted down to scoop up handfuls of silver minnows.

"Once more," ordered Uncle. "We'll catch enough to
take the children fishing in the afternoon." I felt dis-

gruntled and mutinous; and then I remembered where I was and that I was a guest dependent upon them for every mouthful of food I swallowed. Suppose I should anger them, how should I get back to Grand Prairie? We waded back into the lake; and when our feet left the sandy bottom and touched the springy mossiness of deeper water, we turned back again. This time the catch of minnows was smaller. When they had filled their bait buckets, the grownups stowed away their gear in the boat waiting beside the pier. We watched them climb in, watched Uncle Thorvald wrap a cord around the Evinrude starter. Bertina rowed the boat away from the pier, heading the prow into deep water. The motor coughed, stopped, caught, and sputtered noisily in the early morning quiet. The trees cast long morning shadows along the shore line, but the lake had caught fire from the sunrise, and the long swells in the wake of the boat became long golden paths arched across the waters.

"We better go in," suggested Dode. "Mundy'll be waking up for breakfast."

We doused our feet in the bucket standing at the back door, to keep from bringing sand into the cottage. "Why doesn't Uncle just ask us to get up and catch minnows, instead of inviting us for an early swim?" I asked.

"He thinks he's fooling us, I guess," answered Dode, holding the screen door open for me. "We mustn't let him know we catch on. He's too nice to disappoint, don't you think?"

And Uncle was nice, as Dode said, eventually taking us to the sunken island beyond the swampy north end of the 176 lake, where deep green water suddenly gave way to a sandy island submerged in the lake. Anchored here, we could watch the long moss trailing with blossoms blow back and forth in the currents of water; if lucky, we might catch a glimpse of bass, streaking gracefully toward sheltering marine foliage. Uncle, pipe in mouth, pointed out to us a rambling shack where an old Swedish bachelor lived, far up on the hills above the lake. "They call him Crazy Carlson," said Bertina. "He'll follow you around the woods someday. You won't see him, maybe, but you'll hear his steps crashing through ferns and over fallen logs." Dode, Mundy, and I shivered with delight.

On windy days when the waves were too high to fish in the long stretch of water rolling away from the cottage, Uncle took us young savages to the cove, where the wooded sand bar sheltered the water from the strong west wind.

As we pulled away from our pier to cross over to the sheltered cove, the boat rocked up and down in the deep troughs; the motor chugged and sputtered. Dressed in slickers to protect us from the spray, we screamed with delight as the boat breasted the whitecaps and wallowed down into the inclines. Uncle's pipe sent strong puffs of bitter aromatic tobacco blowing in our faces, while he hung on firmly to the tiller of his Evinrude.

When we rounded the sand bar we were suddenly in another world. Sheltered from the strong wind, the cove lay placid and friendly, as though belonging to another time. We fastened minnows or frogs on our hooks and sat staring into the quiet water; for Uncle demanded silence when we fished. Not possessing Uncle's or my sister's patience, I dreamed away the hours under the big brim of my fishing hat, watching puffy clouds move across the deep blue of the Northern sky, hearing the tinkle of cowbells on the wooded isle in back of us, watching the shore beyond, where Bertina or one of the Thorvalsons passed to fetch water from a spring bubbling out of the hillside.

Suddenly there was a bold strike on my line. "Hold it!" bossed Uncle. "Don't reel in yet." He set his pipe on the wide seat beside him. "Play him along for a minute," he said. "Acts like a big one." My line bent sharply downward, the long steep pole a deeply curved arc.

"Now!" I exclaimed. "Can I reel it in?"

"Play it a little longer, Mugs," encouraged Dode, swinging her own steel pole slightly from side to side to show me what Uncle meant.

"Give him a tug," ordered Uncle. As I did, the steel pole smacked the water. "Hold it!" he yelled. "You've either got the bottom of the lake or a big one on the end of that line." Uncle stuck his own pole into the cross planks of the boat. "I'll give you a hand if you need it," he said. "But you ought to land your own. That's the whole point of fishing." He held my pole for a moment to get the feel of the strikes, then handed it back. "Now start to reel in slowly," he ordered.

The whir of the reel was the only sound, except for the gentle splashing of the current against the sides of the boat. The line was heavy. "Reel slowly," warned Uncle. There was a sudden tug, a sudden splash, and the pole kissed water again. "He plays like a bass," Uncle remarked. "Keep on reeling."

Then it seemed as though reel, pole, and line were to be grabbed from my clenched hands. "Hold tight!" barked

Uncle. There was a sharp, explosive pull. At the end of the line a long, tapered, green and silver arrow shot out of the water and plunged back into the green depths, leaving a pool of widening ripples.

"It's a pickerel, Uncle. I saw it," said Dode.

"You take my pole," I said, thrusting it toward Uncle.

"I should say not!" he scoffed, but biting nervously on the stem of his pipe. "You land it. Every fisherman lands his own strike."

"I don't like pickerels," I wailed. "I was fishing for a bass."

"Your orders down underneath must have gotten crossed," said Uncle dryly. "Reel this fellow in, now."

Soon this long, tapered, fighting fish began to surface, its piked snout battling the hook as it snaked and shivered to free itself. "Ease it into my landing net," said Dode, spooning the cupped net into the water under the fighting pickerel. Uncle gave us a hand, and we lowered the floundering fish into the bottom of the boat.

"You want to string him?" asked Uncle, grinning deep furrows on each side of his mouth.

I shivered. "I don't want to touch him. He's long like a snake."

"I'll string him," offered Dode quickly, her long tapering fingers catching the pickerel under the fins and plunging the sharp prong of the stringer into its down-swept mouth and through a fin with an expert flick of her hand. The fish struck at the chain a few times, bobbing the boat slightly, and then he confined himself to sharp, sporadic tugs. When we rounded the sand bar the wind had died down, as it often did before nightfall; the sun was feathering the treetops on the crest of the hills with splashes of pure gold. I felt disappointed that I had not been able to land a sporty bass or a great northern pike; still, I had caught the only fish that afternoon, and Bertina did bake pickerel beautifully, smothering it in tomato sauce, onions, and savory seasoning.

Uncle took the train back to Grand Prairie and the Rekve Store finally; the days slipped into an effortless routine, with Aunt Tina complacent and relaxed. There was milk to fetch in the mornings. Dode, the Thorvalson children, and I climbed the steep hill back of the cottage and took winding cowpaths through ferny woods, stopped to pluck sweet wild strawberries and currants, puckered our mouths at the sharp, prickly taste of gooseberries hidden in thorny bushes.

The fox terrier went along on these excursions, plunging through the thick brush to chase bushy-tailed squirrels, his barks echoing hollowly in the dim woods when he had treed one. We picked bluebells and columbines and lacy ferns, holding our bouquets tightly in perspiring hands, only to throw them away before we reached the Nillson farm on the crest of a steep hill.

Halfway up the steep meadow road that led to the farm, Chummy raced the remaining distance to challenge the shaggy farm dog that barked away intruders upon the Nillson farm; but the old hairy dog knew his job well, and the high-spirited Chummy was finally content to sit at the crest of the hill in unforbidden territory and await the return of the children with their buckets of milk.

Along with the milk, Mrs. Nillson handed us our mail. 180 I picked up a letter from Aunt Gudrun and tore it open eagerly. "Please have a good time," she wrote, "and be a good girl in every way you know best. We miss you a lot. Don't worry—I'm not married yet. Ha! Ha!" I folded the little letter back into the envelope and sighed for a moment, but only for a moment; for Minnesota was, after all, a very special place.

In the evening after the dishes were done, Bertina and Dode took turns rowing about the lake, now fiery in the last glow of sunset. The windows of the cottages glowed like flame and then faded into pearl gray as the sun disappeared behind the rim of hills across the water.

All the sounds of farm and woods were much magnified on the lake: laughter from the cottages on Point Comfort, the leap of a playful fish at our backs, the plunging sound of Bertina's oars and the little dribbling ripples that followed. Lights from the cottages on the shore sent dancing prisms across the blue-black water. We heard the sudden whir of wings above us; and as the birds flew across the point beyond, the lake echoed their hollow laughter. In the land of the Chippewa, the great northern loons wheeled across the night waters.

9

The Pursuit of Culture   Grandma was suspicious of my homework. "So many books?" she asked one afternoon, going through a stack on the kitchen table. "Surely this is not a lesson," she continued, examining a brightly jacketed book. "*Eventyr*," she accused. "Fiction, isn't it?"

"I'm old enough to read it for school now."

"I have no quarrel with the school on any grounds,"

admitted Grandma, whose favorite contention was that if a child had trouble in school he should be given twice as much when he came home. "Well, go ahead. I believe you," she conceded, going on with her work.

So it came about that I began to read everything I could lay my hands on. My accomplice was the pleasant fluttery woman who opened a cubbyhole in the school building once every two weeks and optimistically called it the library. She wore a picture hat upon flaming red hair and stamped the date on our books with a frail blue-veined hand. "Oh dear," she often complained, "if we could only have more books! Doesn't anybody in this town realize the importance of good books?"

Making myself as inconspicuous as possible, I squatted down and examined the dusty shelves for new reading matter, covertly watching Rosa Zimpfelmeier wave a pale hand at half-empty shelves and bewail the lack of culture in Grand Prairie. "And what is it for you, Margarethe?" she asked, holding out her small arm for the book I finally selected, her cupped hand as fragile as a bluebell in a gusty spring rain. "Savonarola!" she exclaimed. "Heavens! I haven't dusted that off for a long time. You sure you want it?" she asked, knowing children shopping for books to take home volumes beyond their mental appetites.

"I think so, Miss Zimpfelmeier," I said timidly, eager to please. "I'm sure I can try it because I read *Mill on the Floss.*"

"And did you like Tom and Maggie and the flood?" she asked, forgetting her role as adviser.

"Oh, I did!" I said, not knowing how to explain how

much I liked George Eliot, and wondering with my analytical timidity if I were expected to do so.

"Well, your next journey will take you to Italy, my dear," said Rosa, "and be sure to tell me if you enjoy it."

If Grandma wondered, the times we were without a hired girl, why I had a sudden interest in doing the supper dishes, why I almost hovered over the table until the family was through the meal, she never made a remark about my reading again. It was spring when I first read *Savonarola*, with the snow water gurgling down the lane and under the planks of the little footbridge to the willow slough, with the warming spring sun traveling slowly across the living room to turn Aunt Gudrun's mahogany music stand into a ruby-paneled box with a golden key on the latch and the picture of Sir Galahad above it so real in the effulgent afternoon sunlight that I expected him and the graceful steed to move on into a shaft of light.

Grandma, sitting pulling threads on an Indian Head tablecloth, looked up. "This is the last cloth I shall ever embroider," she said, her brown-spotted veined hands resting on her fancywork. "I am past eighty, with eyes growing too old to pull threads and weave new ones in place." She picked up her sewing again as if she had been talking about the pot of fruit soup bubbling on the range in the next room. My tears dripped upon the pages of *Savonarola*; for how was I to assure *Bestemor* that she would rock on forever, when in my reading I had discovered that today is but a breath in the long soughing wind of the past? Grandpa came up the cellar steps. We could hear his slow groping steps in the cellarway next to the entry. "Set the table. Quickly, Magrit! Men do not like to wait for meals!" said Grandma.

When Grandma stood above the range, stirring the pot of fragrant soup with a long-handled wooden spoon, we heard Gudrun's quick steps upon the wooden sidewalk. She came in the back door carrying the cold damp freshness of the spring evening upon her fur-trimmed coat. She pulled off a green felt hat and her brown coat and handed them to me to hang in the stair well. "*Mor*, can you ever imagine what happened to me today?"

"*Nei vist*, no indeed, certainly I can't!" laughed Grandma. "I who grow more stupid and dull with every passing day!" She was ladling the soup into deep bowls.

"Do you remember Harry Barnes, the fellow who used to be in the courthouse?"

"Yes, I do," said Grandma, pulling a long pan of brown-crusted rice from the oven, its top studded here and there with cinnamon sticks.

"Well, I had a letter from him today," said Gudrun, a smile crinkling up the corners of her blue eyes, "and he asked me to marry him."

Grandpa looked up from his copy of Rölvaag's *Giants of the Earth*. "I suppose you accepted by return mail?"

"Hardly," said Gudrun. "He's so gushy he makes my skin crawl." I began to relax.

"I thought he was in Bismarck," said Grandpa. "He's a state senator, isn't he?"

"State senator or not! I wouldn't look at him twice. Why, the old rascal's got eight children!"

"And double the number if you married him!" laughed
184 Grandpa.

"Ole!" warned Grandma, inclining her head in my direction. She set down a plate of fresh bread. "Because he has eight children, is that any reason to ridicule the poor man? The more's the pity he doesn't have a wife!"

"You mean you'd throw me at an old fellow like that?" teased Gudrun in mock horror as she wiped her hands on a towel at the sink.

"Come to the table," said Grandma, sitting down. "Certainly I wouldn't throw you at the poor man. He's not a Lutheran, is he?" As though that settled the issue irrevocably.

"Why do you suppose," said Gudrun, sitting down to the table, "I'm always being proposed to by preachers and widowers?"

When I had finished saying the table prayer, Grandpa looked up and smiled. "I'd say that was because, among all mankind, widowers and preachers are often the most confused by women."

That evening after I had gone upstairs to bed I heard Aunt Gudrun at the piano. I leaned on the window sill under the steep eaves, listening to the spring wind's hollow overtones against Aunt Gudrun's simple ballads downstairs. I heard the creak of springs in the bedroom next to mine as Grandpa put his cane beside the bed and settled himself under the covers. The rising moon cast long-tentacled shadows upon the rippling willow slough under my window. Aunt Gudrun's soprano voice was experimenting with wistful longing on the notes of the "Indian Love Call." What did Aunt Gudrun think of at times like this? Was it of Larry, whom she hadn't seen since her days in
Tucson?

My reflections were broken by a stomping from the room beyond. Grandpa's cane tapped imperiously on the floor beside his bed. Aunt Gudrun's plaintive love call broke off suddenly.

"Stop that moonsick cat music!" he bellowed. "Can't a man sleep in his own house?"

From downstairs there was complete silence. What was the matter with *Bestefar?* Then I heard Gudrun's quick steps upon the kitchen floor below, then up into the stair well, and a pause. Was she getting her coat? Grandma's light probing steps sought the upstairs landing.

"Gudrun!" she called. "Gudrun! What are you doing? Why are you putting your coat on? It's late. It's bedtime."

"I don't care what it is, *Mor!*" Gudrun flung back at her. "I don't care if it's midnight!" Her voice broke. "I can't stand it! I'm getting so little out of life lately—and when you can't sing and play in your own home——"

Grandma's voice was tired. "But, Gudrun, he didn't mean anything by that. He's not too well these days. And you know how your father is about music."

"Please, *Mor,* let me go. I have to get out!" Gudrun insisted. The kitchen door banged, and I heard her rapid steps cross the hallway and trip down the back steps. In the moonlight across the muddy field Gudrun's slender figure made its way toward the lights in Uncle Thorvald's house. Grandma's steps climbed the stairway slowly, and I crept into bed. It was strange, this growing up, strange because you could understand how they felt about things: *Bestefar* about being disturbed, *Bestemor* about being upset, and Aunt Gudrun about loneliness.

186 One day Uncle Sven brought all his books over from his

room in the little town where he worked. Grandma let me dust the new bookcase Grandpa had built in the basement workshop and help put the books away on the shelf. Maybe Uncle Sven didn't understand women, but he did understand books. Dickens, Thackeray, Homer, Marcus Aurelius, contemporary novels, and a whole shelf of poetry beckoned me to the corner by the front door. I discovered that there was a poem for every weather, for every day. Among the novels I discovered *The Lamplighter*, and took it under the cottonwoods near where I had seen the mist woman when I was smaller. I read and reread the sentimental story of parted lovers, crossed paths, and the final reunion. The long grasses rippled in the wind; the wild roses bloomed profusely by the fence posts and scented the grassy damp earth. In the great sweep of blue sky above, the billowing clouds of the Northern prairie raced with the west wind.

For several years I had been filling the tar-papered back of Grandpa's chicken house with strange murals of clouds and trees and sky. While Grandpa didn't mind my chalking up the back side of the chicken coop, he drew a line at my scratching up the front, where in a burst of artistic frenzy I had covered the street side with drooping figures of women grinning vacuously. "What you need is a blackboard," he suggested. From the basement one day he brought up a tidy little board complete with chalk rail and nailed it up on the kitchen wall near the stair well. One day I chanced upon a magazine with the inviting command, "Copy me, and you may win a free scholarship in our famous art course." I sat down at Grandma's kitchen table and laboriously sketched a picture of a wicked flapper, folded my drawing into an envelope filched from Grandpa's supply in the library table, borrowed a stamp from Grandma, and went up the grassy lane to town to mail my submission.

For two weeks I must have been the first person in town to hear the train from the East whistle at the crossing by the grain elevators, chug to a stop beside the yellow station, and soon appear through the scattering of trees bordering the meadow back of the Tweiler place. When the train had serpentined across the billowing wheat field and shaken its long tail of cars around the bend near the cemetery, I crawled down from the corner post of the fence and told Grandma that I should be glad to fetch the mail. She suggested that I wait until Mr. Tweiler had had a chance to trundle his wheelbarrow full of mail sacks across the tracks to the post office before I started out. In the post office I stood by the high ink-spattered table and watched Mr. Tweiler's shadow flit behind the opaque little windows of mailboxes.

When he thrust an envelope into 492 with a heavy plop, my trembling fingers dialed open the dusty cubicle. I walked past the Rekve Store and down the street with Grandpa's *Skandinaven* and a long manila envelope tucked under my arm. Down by the willows, where Grandpa's planked footbridge crossed a miniature furrow hollowed out by rain and melting snows, I sat down on the grass and tore open the flap of the envelope.

"We are happy to announce," I read, "that you have won a free primary course in art instruction. If interest and talent prompt you to take our advanced correspondence course, you may order it after the completion of our primary course at a greatly reduced price." Aunt Gudrun, coming down the pathway with a flowered parasol screening her face from a freckling sun, bent down to take the letter from my outstretched hand. "Well, I think it's wonderful!" she exclaimed. "I knew you could do it." We walked in silence to the gate, and when I had it unlatched she said, "Of course you understand we don't know a thing about the Starboard School of Art. Sometimes correspondence course prizes are just a come-on, but it won't hurt to submit your lessons and see. I'm proud you tried," she said, giving me a big smile as I held the back door open for her. Her striped silk taffeta skirt swished gently through the back hall. She propped her parasol beside the kitchen doorjamb, and we went in to eat our lunch.

So I drew the legs of chairs, I drew chairs themselves, I drew chairs with old coats draped over the back. I drew railroad tracks disappearing into infinity. I redrew legs of chairs, I redrew the chairs themselves, and again I draped an old overcoat over the back of the chair. In due order, Book 1, Book 2, Book 3 came through the mail from the great reaches of the Atlantic seaboard and were trundled down Main Street in Mr. Tweiler's wheelbarrow.

Then one Saturday morning when rain and wind pelted in playful gusts across the prairies, I sat at Grandma's kitchen table with my art books. Aunt Tina, a brown coat thrown over her shoulders and her cheeks rosy from the wind, stamped off the moisture in the back porch and came into the kitchen. She smiled at Grandma. "I brought you cookies, Mor," she said.

The fire crackled, kettle sang. Mousy snuggled deep into his blankets by the range. Grandma moved the pot of coffee forward on the stove. I was trying to make the back legs of a chair look farther away than the front legs of the chair.

Aunt Tina took a seat across the table from me. "My girls are doing the Saturday cleaning," she said.

"Ja, I am sure they are; we have good girls," said Grandma. She poured cups of coffee from the granite pot. "It will do you good to stop for the length of a cup of coffee."

"Mor," said Aunt Tina, drawing the air between her teeth with a sort of chirping sound, "how can you who are so saving allow that girl to waste pages and pages of good paper just drawing pictures?"

Grandma put the coffeepot back on the stove and sat down quietly, very quietly, before she replied. "Children must find their joys too, Tina," she said gently.

I picked up the manuals, the paper, the pencils, and climbed to my room above the kitchen. I opened the drop-leaf desk Aunt Gudrun had put upstairs for my very own, deposited my treasures in it, and went over to the window where I could see the rain, willows, and wind locked in sportive combat. For the pursuit of culture, even the Lilliputian culture of childhood, it was necessary to possess hope; and I heard its voice again there. It whispered in the eaves, it gurgled in the rain pipe; and when I sat still enough, I could almost hear God.

O
The Golden Wedding   Another year passed. Aunt Gudrun borrowed the Red Cross tent from the County Fair Commission and had it put under the cottonwoods to the

west of the house. Aunt Tina put up extra beds on the sleeping porch; and except for the prodigious amount of cooking and baking that went on every day, we were ready for Grandpa's and Grandma's fiftieth wedding anniversary.

One of the earliest arrivals was Uncle Olaf and his eight children. Had Uncle Olaf, with his slightly professorial mannerisms and his quiet wife, possessed no other distinction than six girls and two boys, that would have been enough. But Uncle Olaf wore a big heavy black wig, and so far as the younger fry was concerned, that enabled him easily to wear the crown of family distinction. When it was rumored that his toupee reposed on an upturned butter jar at night in order to keep its shape, Uncle Olaf's square-cut wig overshadowed its owner.

Yet it must be said that Uncle Olaf was not a man one glanced at and forgot. Six feet tall, brown-eyed, broad-shouldered, possessor of a fluent and pleasantly caustic tongue, he had an air that easily dominated family gatherings. "He wanted to be a lawyer," said Grandma once, "but the law often lives on the misrepresentation of truth. How can one live a godly life and represent a criminal as innocent?" So Uncle Olaf compromised with his dreams, as, indeed, it seemed to me all adults had at one time or another, and spent his days balancing the ledgers of mercantile firms and counting the little chins that munched the food around the family table.

Once he strode past an upstairs clothes closet in our house, glanced at my dresses swinging from their wooden hangers, and said, "Tish, tish—you have more dresses than 192 all my girls put together." Grandma, who set a good deal of store by even the spontaneous outbursts of her sons, never forgot that remark, much to my sorrow. His girls, by the economic necessity inherent in rearing most large families, cheerfully wore each other's hand-me-downs and whispered among themselves in the conspiratorial manner of large and close-knit families.

An afternoon train brought new arrivals: Aunt Nellie, Uncle Henry, and my brother Carl from Tucson. Aunt Nellie was full of tales about her recent perilous descent on the back of a mule into the Grand Canyon of Arizona. Uncle Sven, especially, found Aunt Nellie's reiterated accounts of her trip to Phantom Ranch particularly hilarious. "Didn't think a mule would ever have put up with her," he remarked laconically. "Between all her extra pounds and her constant chatter, you'd think he would have pitched her overboard."

"Sven!" reprimanded Grandma. "We like Nellie. She's a good woman."

"Sure she is," admitted our confirmed bachelor, "but how was the mule to know that?"

One evening a Dodge parked beside the willows outside; and when I saw the Wisconsin license plates I knew who it was: my father, his brother Gabriel, and some of Gabriel's children. Was it imagination, or did the family, sitting on chairs enjoying the cool shade of the afternoon, stiffen as families often do when someone in the family but outside the charmed circle arrives? Old as I was now, I had a strong longing for Grandpa's lap and his protecting arms, as I had sought them in the past when my father visited. Smiling but reticent, he shook hands with all of us, Aunt Gudrun giving her hand and attention for only

the most cursory greeting, and excusing herself to perform some indoor tasks.

Sitting upon the grass beside Grandpa's rocker, I covertly watched my father and his people, fighting the same feeling of fright and confusion his earlier visits had engendered. Was he good-looking? Did I resemble him in any way? Perhaps if I watched him closely I should discover his most characteristic mannerisms, so that never in Aunt Gudrun's presence should I reflect them; for it seemed imperative that, since Aunt Gudrun bristled so visibly when he was about, I must never in any way remind her of him. His brother Gabriel I liked because I dared approach him as a person, not as a character in a family drama, subtle and undercover as the play was. Uncle Gabriel had a spontaneous warmth, a quickness of reaction, a quiet vitality I admired. Why couldn't I feel the same way about my father? Why did his dark hair, his gray-brown eyes, his nervous gait and speech strike the warning bell of subconscious dislike? I wanted to get my sister Dode aside and talk the matter over with her; but visitors came and went through our homes, crossed the cornfield between the houses, and talked incessantly as families will talk when thrown together.

Finally the tables were set in Aunt Tina's big yard on the side of the house between the fir trees and the mock orange bushes. Here Grandma and Grandpa, now grown bent and tired and gray, celebrated another wedding day, thousands of miles away from the high-steepled Ullensvang church above the Hardanger Fjord, where they had been married fifty years ago. During the greetings of well-wishers and family, they furtively dabbed at escaping tears and smiled the sweet sad smiles of the old, who see the end of their voyage before the new land is sighted. Among the guests moved my tall and stately great-aunt, Grandpa's baby sister, who with her lovely walk and her deep melodious voice seemed to epitomize the grace and beauty of the best Norwegian women. Uncle Ole, her husband, had remained at home with his bank account; but she had brought my brother Alfred along, who seemed as strange to me as my father.

When some of the guests had departed and our households had a semblance of order again, the wind commenced to blow from the southeast, bringing a hot arid breeze that always produced a violent headache in Grandma, sometimes sending her to bed. She had planned to walk up to Aunt Tina's for coffee but, when the time approached, found herself much too exhausted to walk across the field. I was sent to announce that Grandma had taken to her bed. The usually clear blue sky with its scattering of puffy, wandering clouds had disappeared, and high above the wilting corn fronds the sun glared brassily. The grass, lush and green only a few days ago, crackled under my feet in Aunt Tina's back yard. Living close to the earth, as children do, I hated every dragging hour of these torrid days, longing for the customary fresh winds of Dakota.

Aunt Tina's neat kitchen was deserted; and when I was about to call to rouse them, I heard Aunt Nellie's deep voice remark, "It's a pity she had to die. I've always felt, when it's a choice of saving a mother or child, the mother ought to be saved. How did it happen they saved Margaret's life instead of her mother's?"

When I turned to leave they heard my fleeing steps. "Is that you, Mugs?" called Aunt Tina. She came to the doorway from the dining room. "Where's your grandma?"

"She—she had a headache," I said.

"Don't go. Don't go," said Aunt Tina. "The girls are gone, and I need a pail of water from Stone's well."

Every child accepts his existence as his right, no matter how bewildering circumstances regarding that existence might be, and I stood shocked by the revelation that existence itself had been a matter determined not by Deity but by adults such as the two aunts visiting over coffee cups.

"Go after some water, please," said Aunt Tina, handing me the pail. At her command, spoken from a complacent but rather determined face, I felt an overwhelming birth of revolt.

"It's just too hot to carry a pail of water for a whole block," I said. When the words had been spoken I was as much surprised as my auditors.

"Well," said Aunt Nellie, coming to dock against the wooden piling of the sink, "Grandma will hear of this, Margaret."

"I know," I said. I took one more look at Aunt Tina's face, now alerted to an expression of sudden shock, and fled out through the sleeping porch to the blistering back yard.

Home under the cottonwoods, I sought the peace and safety of the yard swing. Even the trees sounded different on such a day, clattering restlessly in their leafy tops. The Plymouth Rocks in the pen at the back of the lot squatted in the sandy shade and fought among themselves and 197 pecked irritably at their feathers. The green shade up in

Uncle Sven's room sucked at the open window, flapped awkwardly in a sudden spurt of hot wind, and then flattened against the screen.

When I heard a car, I looked up to see my father's coupe heading for a parking place beside our fence. "You haven't talked with me at all," he had said only yesterday; and measuring the distance between the fence and the back door and the back door and the yard swing, I leaped from the swing and raced for the house. What words did I have to share with this stranger? What compromise with the kind of peace I had found in Grandpa's house would I be obliged to make if I shared my plans and activities with this disturbing stranger, who had returned again to find his children alien? I took the stairs two at a time and dashed for Grandma's darkened bedroom.

"*Er det du?* Is it you?" she asked needlessly. "How did you find it up at Aunt Tina's?"

"*Bestemor,*" I said breathlessly, "Aunt Tina told me to fetch fresh water from Stone's well, and I wouldn't go." Grandma's pale face looked up at me from a lace-bordered pillow.

"That I cannot believe," she said, rising on an elbow. "What did you tell her?"

"I'm tired of people and talking and heat!" I cried.

"*Ja, ja vist.* We might all be that," she said, rising and placing her feet uncertainly upon the worn carpet demoted from the living room to service upstairs. "But to give way to such feelings is not Christian. Might we not believe that Aunt Tina, too, is tired—tired of a houseful of company and the incessant chatter? Tired of cooking even for 198 you and me the many times we have sat at her table?

When we share our pleasures and duties, pleasure increases and duty diminishes for all of us."

"Aunt Nellie is going to come down and tell you I was disobedient. She said so."

"Maybe she will," said Grandma, running her palms over her thinning hair and rising unsteadily to her feet. "But if you will soon run up to Aunt Tina's and tell her you were sorry you did not obey, the words Aunt Nellie might speak to me need have no power over you." She brushed the wrinkles out of her skirt and started toward the hallway. "Come," she said, "the sooner such an errand is done, the lighter is its burden. I have some dishes here you may return, and you may carry the words you must speak upon the dishes." She smiled and so did I, for often the young and old can meet in allegory.

That evening an opal sky with overtones of mauve discolored all the familiar things about the house and in the yard. Not a thing upon the visible earth moved. The cottonwoods stood silenced from their eternal clattering. The long grasses beside the fence were frozen in a dusty rigidity.

Seated upon the grass—I beside Aunt Gudrun, fanning herself with a newspaper—we sat like stick figures under the enveloping dome of a gigantic discolored sky. The birds, whose chitchat had always been the evening's lullaby, were utterly silent. Mousy, the gray angora, stroked against our stretched-out legs, then knelt upon the hot grass beside us and regarded the strange world with slitted eyes. The sound of a door slamming shut in some neighbor's house came to us with a hollow echoing sound. There was no evening, no long Northern twilight; the fantastic sky faded into a murky, starless black, and the heat from sky and earth settled heavily upon us.

"When it breaks," a voice spoke softly from the darkness, "it will be a terror. I've never seen a day like this end except in violence." I moved closer to Aunt Gudrun, who stroked listlessly the fur of the silent, still cat. To the east and south heat lightning billowed across the sky in waves of yellow flares, lighting up stratum after stratum of piled-up clouds. To the west sharp prongs of bursting flame forked across the miles of dark and silent farmland. I shivered and edged close to Gudrun and Grandma.

"You cannot sleep in the tent tonight!" said Grandpa to Aunt Gudrun.

"We'll see," said Aunt Gudrun in a strangely stubborn voice.

Like two avenging armies, the lightning in the east and the lightning in the west charged toward the dome of the sky. A faint warm wind set up a rustling in the grass.

"I'm going to bed," said Grandpa, rising stiffly in a burst of light from the flaring sky.

"How can men go to sleep on a night like this!" exclaimed Aunt Gudrun. "If you *could* go to sleep in that oven of a house, you'd only be awakened by the storm!" A distant sound, like a faraway waterfall, rolled in across the prairies. The willows suddenly slashed their branches, and the cottonwoods set up a deep, hollow murmuring.

"*Det kommer.* It comes," said Grandma. "The tent has been made secure?" she asked, getting to her feet as she leaned upon my shoulder.

"The men looked after it!" said Aunt Gudrun, rising 200 quickly to her feet and scooping Mousy into her arms.

"Come on," she said. "Let's go into the basement." In the house she stopped long enough to fetch some candles from the pantry shelf. "Help Grandma down the steps."

Grandma stood undecided for a moment. Then she shrugged. "There's no use talking to Ole," she said. "He's as content in his own bed, come wind or weather, as he'll be anywhere else. He might not even awaken." Taking Grandma's arm, I helped her down the steep, narrow stairs. How slight she seemed, I thought, this sweet, aging woman of strong will. "Please, God," I quickly prayed, "go with her wherever she goes."

The dim globe of light above us, shining above Grandpa's carpenter bench, quickly snuffed out; and a roaring, keening screech blocked voice, sense, and thought. The house seemed to tense above us and then settled down into a flapping, swaying, rattling bedlam. I hung onto Grandma's arm. A candle flickered, wavered, and grew into a fluttering flame. The cellar window above the carpenter bench burst in a clatter of shattering glass, and a cold wind rushed in upon us. The candle blew out.

"Thank God!" exclaimed Grandma. "The worst is over. But somewhere people have not fared as well."

"That's right, *Mor*," said Gudrun, cupping a new flame of candlelight. "We were on the edge of a tornado. Probably followed its usual track south of us." Rain pelted the ground outside and the windowpanes in the furnace room like stones thrown by prankish gods of the Northland.

"You'll never sleep outdoors tonight," said Grandma. "In such a wind as we have had your beds will be soaked."

"Where else will we sleep?" asked Gudrun, propping a board against the open window. "The rest will be coming back from Aunt Tina's, Gabriel and her father, and——"

"Gudrun," said Grandma, "Magrit's father will be glad to give you his bed and sleep upon the couch in the kitchen."

Gudrun, plaiting her waist-long hair for bed, suddenly turned toward Grandma and said, "I would never sleep in his bed. Never, *Mor!*" Gudrun's eyes were bright with scorn. "Have you forgotten that, if it were not for him, our sister would still be alive?"

Outside the wind beat against the foundation of the old house. In the cellar the candle which Gudrun had set in the vise on Grandpa's bench cast long grotesque shadows upon the cemented walls. They saw me then, standing wide-eyed and still beside a shelf filled with home-canned fruits and pickles.

"The storm is dying, Gudrun," said Grandma. "Let's go upstairs and see what's left of things above."

Gudrun's hand was quick to rest upon Grandma's arm. "I know how well built that big Red Cross tent is, *Mor*. You'll see, our beds are dry. You go to bed, Mother." When had the quick-spirited Gudrun ever spoken so softly?

21

Journey of Hope   Harvey Blayne stopped Aunt Gudrun in one of the dim corridors of the county courthouse. "How are you and the boss making it these days?" he asked.

"Snowed under with work," admitted Gudrun.

The tall, lean county attorney smiled down at her.

"Why don't you run for office next election?" When she started to shake her head, he raised the palm of his hand in a negative gesture. "I mean it, Gudrun," he said. "As deputy clerk, you're doing a lion's share of the work now."

"Of course Fred isn't really well," agreed Gudrun. "He's a partially disabled veteran. I don't think I'd feel right about it, Harvey." She shifted a stack of papers to the other arm.

"The wife thinks it's a swell idea," he persisted.

"Yes, some of the women would, at least a lot of them in town, Harvey. But can you see some of the farmers and old-timers voting for a woman clerk of court? Why, they'd consider it indecent for me to be up in the courtroom when some unsavory case is being tried. As if I'm not there anyway!" she laughed.

"And who has the key to the vault? Now 'fess up, Gudrun, haven't you spent many a rainy day poring over the more exciting files?"

"I'd like to find the time!" she scoffed.

"Well, think it over." Harvey started down the hall, then turned. "Don't let running against Fred worry you. He has a farm and other resources to depend on, but you can use that extra salary, Gudrun."

"Thanks, Harvey. What's really bothering me, though," said Gudrun, "are Miss Sabin's horrid arithmetic problems."

"You too!" roared Harvey delightedly. "Tommy and I were up until eleven with those darn things."

"Can't something be done?" asked Gudrun. "Hasn't anyone talked with the girl?"

"I understand someone did. All he got out of Miss Sabin

was that she was 'well within the course of study.' " He mocked the schoolteacher's diction.

"You can imagine what her stiff arithmetic assignments are doing to Margarethe!" laughed Gudrun. "She has always been hopeless in mathematics, but never to the point of insomnia."

"Miss Sabin is undoubtedly bright enough," admitted the county attorney, "but why call attention to it by assigning such terrific arithmetic lessons? I'll venture to say half the parents in Grand Prairie are sitting up half the night trying to do eighth-grade arithmetic."

But down at Grandma's house arithmetic was, for the moment, forgotten.

"But it's still my hair," I insisted, watching Ragna, the hired girl, set the table for supper.

Ragna's serene, attractive face was puckered in a frown. "Maybe it is your hair," she said. "Still, I hate to be here when your grandma comes home for supper and sees that you've cut most of it off." Ragna reached up in the warming oven and took out a plate of cinnamon rolls, fragrant and shiny with sugar glaze. "Your grandma thought the world of your hair, combing it and braiding it every morning and washing it on Saturdays."

"With kerosene," I added.

"All right, with kerosene," said Ragna seriously, "but it didn't hurt it none. I think you did wrong cutting it off. Honestly I do."

"You've got bobbed hair, Ragna."

"That's different. I'm my own boss, but you're still a 204 youngster."

"You look awfully pretty with bobbed hair," I hinted.

"Maybe so," said Ragna honestly. "But you looked a lot prettier with your big brown braids looped up in ribbons." She peered out the window. "Say, here comes your grandma now. Guess I'll go upstairs and powder my nose before supper. Shut the damper on the stove a little if it begins firing too hard."

In the mirror above the sink I took a quick, furtive glimpse at the new creature. If only I could have the hair which now lay on Mr. Vogel's barbershop floor and miraculously put it back in place before Grandma's soft steps on the sidewalk took her into the kitchen! My straight hair hung like a fringe over my left ear, looped stiffly across my forehead, and fell over my right ear like rain water off a steep roof.

Grandma stood in the kitchen. I looked at Grandma, and Grandma looked at me. Her firm little chin grew firmer; and for a moment the heat lightning of her glance shimmered across the distance between us. "*Store verden!*" she exclaimed. "Great world! What have you done!" She walked over to the settee under the clock and set down her parcels.

"Could I help you off with your coat, *Bestemor*, and hang it up for you?"

Grandma put her wrinkled hands up to her thinning hair and pulled off the black sailor hat she always wore for occasions like attending church, ladies' aid, or coffee parties. Still she said nothing. She thrust a long black hatpin back into the hat, walked past me, and started up the stairway, the iambic beat of her shuffling steps echoing in the quiet kitchen.

Slowly I returned to the mirror above the sink and, like the queen in the fairy tale, begged the glass to flatter my fears away. But I saw a pug nose grown even more pugged by the squared-off effect of my hair; and without the softening flattery of braids and ribbon, the pale freckles across my nose seemed to leap to attention. Then I hated Janice and Lucy and all the girls in my class who had been after me for weeks to cut my hair and leave it in the tobacco ashes and dust on Mr. Vogel's linoleum floor. I could imagine my sister Dode up at Aunt Tina's right now setting the table for supper, her long copper hair caught loosely in the back with a bright clasp or hair ribbon. What I wouldn't give to look like that again! I sat down in Grandma's high-backed rocker, the cold wood scratching my bare neck, while I fought back tears of disgust and regret. Ragna's quick steps bounced down the stairway.

"What did your grandma say?" she asked.

"Nothing, that's the trouble, nothing," I said.

"Oh well," comforted Ragna, "it can always grow out again."

"How long will it take? A few months?"

"At least a year," said Ragna, checking on the progress of her dinner. *Bestemor* could die in a year, I thought, and she would never comb my heavy braids again; for lately she had begun to talk of leaving this world as a traveler would talk, with his bags neatly packed and the arrangements made for his journey. Only a week ago when we had been reading Norwegian tales together, she had said, "To leave this world must be like taking the cattle up to the *saeter* to graze in the summer. The farther one climbs up the rocky hillside, the clearer and cleaner becomes the

view, as it always becomes when one lives closer to God. Sometimes I feel as I did when young, as though I had climbed into the lovely mountains of peace again; and I can see the worries and fatigues and bothers of my younger years as evils of the mind and the flesh."

Now in the kitchen, in the moment of my humiliation, I could hear the tread of her descending steps. She spoke to Ragna. "It's good to have a girl like you, Ragna," she said in Norwegian. "I have been gone all afternoon, yet I can come home and find the house warm and fragrant with cooking and know the family is better cared for than I could do it myself."

"Here is your chair, *Bestemor*," I said. "Don't you want to sit down?"

"*Og du*," said Grandma, turning from the beaming Ragna. "And you," she said, looking at me, "I have a parcel for you." She went over to the settee and fingered among some packages. "Thorvald himself waited on me in the store when I stopped after ladies' aid." She handed me a small package. I tore the string on the brown wrapping paper and pulled out a yard of red and green plaid ribbon.

"What is it for, *Bestemor?*" I asked, but I knew already.

"It was bought for your hair," she said, "but you had best lay it away in your drawer with the rest of your pretty ribbons."

"I didn't go to Mr. Vogel's barbershop without permission, *Bestemor*," I said. "I want you to know I went way up to the courthouse after school with some of the girls and asked Aunt Gudrun. She said if I had really thought it over and was sure I wanted it short to go ahead. She really did, *Bestemor*."

"I am sure of that," said Grandma. "But do you yourself really like it?"

"I hate it!" I cried, rushing into her arms. I felt her hand rise to stroke my hair as she always did when she comforted me; but the hand only rested upon my shoulder.

"When we come to problems like yours," she said, "it is well to search oneself and ask if what we want is in keeping with what we have. For you," she said softly, "shining braids and ribbons still go with a girl who bends her head over fairy tales and talks with the spirits of her imagination. Remember, where the conscience must struggle, the warning is strong and clear."

That evening as the grownups sat with coffee cups and I was bent over the kitchen table with arithmetic problems, I heard Aunt Gudrun announce that she was to be a delegate to the national Red Cross convention. "And I'll stop off in New York and see Larry!" she exulted. "I'll even get to spend a few days with his people in Pennsylvania!" Her voice, laced with song, threaded through the conversation, always returning to the trip to Washington and her chance to see Larry, whom she had not seen since her stay in Tucson. Uncle Sven, home for the night, stood in the doorway between the dining end of the kitchen and the living room.

"Well, Mugs," he teased, "you can kiss your Aunt Gudrun good-by for good. When an old maid travels on an errand of romance, she takes a fast train."

"Sven," she said, growing earnest for a change, "you know most of the farmers in your township. Think they'd go for a woman clerk of court?"

"Those mossbacks?" he scorned. "What's the matter? Bitten by ambition suddenly?"

"Well, you never know about the future," she admitted seriously, "and Fred's getting hard to work for—seems to have a chip on his shoulder. Needs my help and resents it at the same time. Harvey Blayne and some of the other fellows up there want me to run for office the next time."

They were in the kitchen now. "I'll help you all I can," Uncle Sven promised, propping his feet against the grate and studying the glowing coals in the firebox. I had a sudden surge of hope. If Aunt Gudrun planned to run for office, perhaps she wasn't planning to get married! But why was she so eager to see Larry if nothing could come of it?

"I think the folks are against it, Mother especially," confided Gudrun in a low voice, "but I could use the salary. I'm already doing most of the work." Aunt Gudrun sat down on the settee, strangely idle for one whose hands were always busy. "How are the problems?" she asked, turning her glance my way.

"I can't get them!" I wailed. "What good is all this stuff ever going to do me? Square root and compound interest—anything she can think up to keep us from passing!"

"Miss Sabin," said Uncle Sven, "is that the pretty little blonde who sings alto in the choir?"

"Yes, that's the one," said Aunt Gudrun.

"Is she the one the preacher's sweet on?" asked Uncle Sven.

"Oh no!" I interrupted as Gudrun was about to reply. "That's Miss Wimple, our music teacher. The girls all say that——"

"Better stick to your arithmetic," suggested Aunt Gudrun dryly.

"Maybe she wouldn't be so hell-bent on showing her

brains if she had a little love in her life," said Uncle Sven, filling his pipe from a can of Prince Albert smoking tobacco. That would be a relief, I thought, to have Miss Sabin so preoccupied with other matters that she had little time to dabble with trapezoids, excavate cellars to determine the number of cubic feet of dirt removed, paper living rooms, and dig wells—all on blackboard and paper. It was bad enough being ignorant in arithmetic, but now I had to worry about Aunt Gudrun and her trip as delegate to the Red Cross meeting in Washington.

During the next few weeks Aunt Gudrun was too busy shopping for dresses and hats, planning her itinerary, doing up extra work in the office to help me with my problems. I crossed the field to Aunt Tina's and sought out my sister Emily.

"I think Miss Sabin has gone crazy!" said Dode. "Everyone's talking about the way she throws arithmetic assignments at your class. You know what I think?" she asked earnestly. "I think she's mad because you kids take your work home to your parents. I think she figures if Grand Prairie wants to work arithmetic at night she'll give them some real problems to do. Anyway, that's how Uncle Thorvald figures it."

"Do you suppose I'll be in eighth grade again?" I asked.

"Your other grades are good," said Dode slowly. "Mugs, I don't mean to be critical," said my sister, "but why can't you use the same thinking in arithmetic you use to parse a sentence and do your diagrams? Why, you even understand when to use 'he' and 'him' and 'I' and 'me' in sentences, like 'between you and me.' That takes brains," she encouraged. "Why can't you do arithmetic?"

"I don't know," I said, my head propped woefully between the palms of my hands, "but maybe Miss Sabin is right. She says my head must have compartments, one for grammar, one for reading, and a small one for mathematics. She even wondered if I don't slam the door shut on the arithmetic compartment soon's I say the word."

It was not so long before the day of Aunt Gudrun's departure for the convention that the eighth-grade class awoke to the miracle of love. Miss Sabin, her blond hair curling delicately over her furrowed temples, told us that we had, perhaps, been traveling through arithmetic with more speed than necessary. When the dark-skinned newcomer in the eighth grade bent over *The Vision of Sir Launfal* and read in his halting, frightened voice, "He mussed as he sat," Miss Sabin smiled indulgently and suggested he meant "mused," explaining pleasantly that when two consonants followed a vowel like u the vowel had a short sound. Janice peered across the aisle and raised a questioning eyebrow in my direction. Some of the rest of us who habitually sat like icicles in a freeze of despair began to thaw perceptibly.

In the afternoon, when Miss Wimple came in to teach us as little music as the law allowed, she brushed past Miss Sabin like a tenderfoot meeting a sidewinder in a box canyon. "I know what's the matter," whispered Janice when Miss Wimple's back was turned to the blackboard. "Mother said Miss Sabin's going with Reverend Kjelland now, as of last night." Maybe our minister himself didn't know it, but so far as the eighth-grade class in Grand Prairie's grammar school was concerned, he had demonstrated how it was possible for love to overcome evil.

212

Soon the very hour of Aunt Gudrun's departure was approaching. How could I bear her absence, she whose voice was rippled with laughter, who would warm my heart with foolish pleasantries as I had warmed her bed these many years?

As Ragna was beginning to dish up the supper, we heard Gudrun's quick steps upon the walk below the kitchen window. We heard her stomp the mud off her rubbers in the back entry. When we opened the kitchen door for her, there were marks of tears upon her face.

"What is it, Gudrun?" asked Grandma, going toward her quickly.

A sob broke from Gudrun's throat as she flung her coat upon the settee. "*Mor!* I'm not going!" she cried. "I'm all packed and my ticket's bought and I'm not going!"

"Why not, Gudrun, why not?" asked Grandma.

"Fred says he has business out of town more pressing than my going to the convention, if you can believe that," she said.

"But why—but why would he do that?" persisted Grandma.

"*Gud vist,* God knows!" said Gudrun. "Maybe he couldn't bear the thought of me going on that expense-paid trip. Maybe he has heard rumors that people are trying to get me to run against him when the next election comes. I don't know."

"Can't someone stop him from upsetting all your plans?" suggested Grandma gently. "Someone on the Red Cross board?"

"He can be stopped, I suppose," said Gudrun. "But so can my job."

"Well, it seems a pity," said Grandma. "You've waited so long for a vacation like this—for any vacation."

Ragna called us to supper. We sat down, feeling the burden of Gudrun's disappointment. "Can you see now, *Far*," said Gudrun, turning her face toward Grandpa's, "can you see why I want to run against him? That little big shot!" she exclaimed. "Letting me make all my plans to go to Washington, letting me make my plans to visit Larry in New York and his people in Pennsylvania, letting me work overtime into the evening to clean up all the extra work in the office—and then walking in tonight and saying I'd simply have to drop all plans to leave, that he had to look after his farm and I'd have to stay and tend to his office."

That night I wondered—had God answered my prayers or hadn't He? I had prayed more than once that Aunt Gudrun would not leave; but I didn't like to think of that now, with Gudrun muffling her sobs in the pillow beside me and the light from the cold fall moon shining on the glass of Larry's picture upon Aunt Gudrun's dresser. I didn't want to think of anything but Aunt Gudrun lying quietly beside me, trying not to awaken me because there was school the coming morning.

22

The Governor   "Stop fretting about it, Gudrun," comforted Grandma. "We'll never have a dining room in this house, in our time, anyway."

"Well, it does seem a little peculiar, inviting the governor to dinner in our kitchen."

"No, I don't think so," argued Grandma, rocking contentedly by the range. "He came of Norwegian immigrant people. He has eaten in kitchens before."

Aunt Gudrun turned her empty coffee cup upside down upon the saucer, twirled the inverted cup around to the count of three, and peered into the massed grounds with a narrowed squint of her eyes.

"What do you see? Is the governor coming to dinner?" I asked excitedly.

Aunt Gudrun looked up at me and smiled, laughter crinkles forming at the edges of her eyes. "I'm afraid all I see are lumps of grounds that look like my Plymouth Rocks. I'll have to go down in the cellar and ask *Far* to kill two or three of our plumpest fryers."

"You try to do too much," reprimanded Grandma. "Your job in the courthouse, work at home in the evenings —the Red Cross, the choir and the organ——" She studied her old veined hands. "In my time, too, I have worked and counted daily tasks a blessing, but to work as though driven and to run from one event to another—well, what if the governor is coming to speak on Reformation Sunday, let others with homes more elaborate entertain him——"

"I wouldn't have it any other way," admitted Gudrun. "I like to be with people. I have never liked solitude."

Grandma nodded resignedly and picked up her knitting. I finished cracking a bowl of walnuts for Aunt Gudrun's baking. Suddenly Grandma's gentle rocking ceased, and her gray-brown eyes under a broad and wrinkled brow looked worried. "Gudrun, could I be taking too much Beef, Iron, and Wine?" she asked earnestly.

Gudrun's broad smile considered Grandma's question. "Why, *Mor*, do you feel tipsy?" she laughed.

215

"*Nei vist*, nothing like that," Grandma replied with haste. "I can't really explain what I mean to say, but I feel as though something is eating my insides. *Ja vist!* What else can one expect?" she asked with a gentle shrug of her shoulders. "Our mortal bodies must wear out."

"Could I take you to see Dr. Whitaker?"

"No, no," said Grandma. "It will pass, as all things pass." Her knitting needles were the only sound in the kitchen as Aunt Gudrun studied her recipe book and I sat sketching the bare-limbed willows in the little slough beyond the kitchen window. "He isn't coming very often these week ends," said Grandma, as though she were continuing an uninterrupted conversation.

"Who? Sven?" asked Aunt Gudrun, though there was no need to ask whom Grandma meant.

"*Ja*, Sven," said Grandma.

"So that's what's bothering your stomach!" exclaimed Gudrun with a lighthearted attempt at badinage. "Don't worry, Mor, he's a grown-up man; he has friends."

"A man may be grown," said Grandma, "and still be but a child in some respects. St. Paul has said, 'Take on the whole armour of faith.'" She sighed. "He must have known how easy it is for the soul to be like a piece of fruit —good to look at, firm to the touch, but bearing unseen the germs of its destruction." She saw me at the table then, having forgotten I was there. She lowered her eyes.

"Shall we have pie for dessert Sunday?" asked Gudrun brightly.

"Anything at all you like. I myself have never enter-
216 tained a governor," replied Grandma.

How strange adults were! I thought. Why shouldn't I know what was wrong with Uncle Sven lately? Couldn't I smell his breath too? "Worse than a woman waiting for a seafaring man to come home is the woman waiting for a drunken husband," Grandma had often remarked. "The hunger for the sea makes a livelihood, but hunger for alcohol loses a livelihood."

Yet even I could see that, if Uncle Sven liked to drink, his bachelorhood was a blessing. And even though I had moments of violent dislike for Uncle Sven, when swagger and boasting healed the wounds of his ego, still I could sense the gap between the human dream and the human act. I read the volumes he had patiently collected, walked for a moment along the banks of the Tiber with Marcus Aurelius, sailed on Pope's iambic pentameter along the wooded shores of Ithaca, and wept over a grandfather's death in *The Old Curiosity Shop*. A man must love books to return to their reading as to the home of an understanding friend; a man must have a hope and a dream who reads the literature of hopes and dreams. But a man who leaves a mother weeping silently in an old rocking chair in the fading dusk of a winter's afternoon, and a man whose father wipes away a tear with the awkward whisk of his shirt sleeve—that man is possessed by a force beyond his own strength. It was then, and only then, I could not like Uncle Sven.

My thoughts were interrupted by steps in the porch beyond the kitchen. Bertina opened the door and smiled. "Hello," she said and then, looking embarrassed, "Gudrun, may I speak to you alone?"

"Come in, of course!" invited Gudrun. "We'll go upstairs." Bertina gave us a halfhearted smile and followed Aunt Gudrun up the stairway.

"What's wrong, *Bestemor?*" I whispered. "A man again?"

Grandma shook her head with disapproval, but there was laughter behind her eyes. I took her hand. "But, *Bestemor*, not telling me things will never keep me from knowing. I know Aunt Tina has always scolded my sister when she wants to go out with the boys, and when she stands out on the steps with Ronnie in the moonlight, Aunt Tina acts as if they're up to some wickedness."

Grandma pushed me toward the pantry. "Let's make a cake for Aunt Gudrun," she suggested. "It will do more good than discussing other people's business." She picked up her Pillsbury cookbook. "Now what should you like to try?" she invited, leafing through the book.

"Oh, anything," I replied. "But how did Aunt Tina herself ever marry if she never stood out in the moonlight with Uncle Thorvald?"

"Let's make a white walnut-filled cake," she suggested. When she had reached into one of the cupboards for the flour sifter she smiled. "We might have need of such a one as Christina when your time to look at the moon comes."

"Oh no, *Bestemor*," I said as I swung open the flour bin. "I think Aunt Gudrun would be much, much better for that." We worked in silence, Grandma's steps shuffling softly on the linoleum floor of the pantry. How comfortable and unhurried she was!

"Ex-shus me," she said as she knocked my hand, which
218 held the measuring spoon.

"*Bestemor*," I laughed. "For years and years I've been trying to help you say 'excuse' instead of 'ex-shus.'"

"*Ja*, and should I live for a hundred more I should not be able to pronounce such a word. It is like my Ole with his *j*, for no matter how much you laugh, he will always ask you to pass the yell-lee."

"All you have to do is practice, and the words will come out right."

Grandma finished greasing the cake tin. "Is that what I rocked your cradle for and nursed you from death by whooping cough, that you should live to be ashamed of one who speaks with such simplicity?"

I threw my floury hands about her waist and hugged her fiercely. "No, it is not!" I cried. "It is only that you are so perfect to me, I never want anyone unkind or cruel to laugh at you!"

"And who laughs?" she asked, pouring coffee beans into the grinder.

"No one, *Bestemor!* No one!"

"And if they did," asked Grandma, "would that be any cause for you or me to be hurt? One must walk in his own way with the love of God in his heart, and then what the world may say is but a weak and silly sound in one's ears."

She walked into the kitchen and bent down to examine the temperature gauge on the crackling range. I blinked to fight away the tears. I heard steps on the landing above. "Stay and have some coffee," suggested Aunt Gudrun. "Even if you don't drink coffee, have some cookies with us."

But Bertina only shook her head and smiled. She came

up beside me and put her arm about my waist. "Tomorrow you can help me grade English papers," she promised.

"Do you suppose I can?" I asked with pride. How did Bertina know I liked to do that better than anything else in the world right now? I fervently hoped that Bertina, who was now teaching seventh and eighth grades in a nearby town, had been extra hard on her charges, and that the papers extended in a pile to the ceiling.

"We miss you, Bertina," said Grandma, "now that you are a young woman and out making your mark in the world."

"A teacher never makes much of a mark, *Bestemor*. But I did turn some strapping farm boys over on my knee and give them a whipping!" laughed Bertina. "And do you know what? Their parents came and thanked me!"

"They're farmers' children," said Grandma wisely, "and a farmer knows both colt and child need to feel the reins that direct them."

When Bertina left, Aunt Gudrun smiled and said, "She's a lovely girl. I am growing old, *Mor*, when the children come to me for advice in love. It was trouble with Tina over Ronnie again," she explained.

"When women weep, it is always a man," said Grandma, settling down into her rocker again. She turned around and looked at the clock. It was easy to see what she was thinking about. If Sven was coming, he would be here any moment or not at all. I poured the batter into the loaf pan. "Put it well in the center on the upper shelf," admonished Grandma. Then she heard the steps upon the walk below, for her ears were as keen as the ears of a young girl. "He's here," she said. "Sven's here." I closed the oven door quickly, to put the cake safely in before the kitchen door blew the evening's cold into the room.

"Hello!" called Sven. "Can you put up a visitor this week end, Mor?"

"*Ja vist,*" she said. "There is always a room for you, Sven," but there was no need to reply, for her face was luminous with joy.

"I have a surprise for you in the car, Mugs," he said.

"What is it?"

"My Edison phonograph."

"Have you tired of it so quickly?" asked Gudrun, coming in from the living room.

"No, just tired of the records I have, and I'll leave it here until I can buy some more." He turned to me. "I have 'The Whistler and His Dog,' 'Every Little Movement'— there's a whole case of cylinders, but just be sure you slip them back in the cardboard protectors when you are through playing."

Grandma opened the oven door with caution. "I can always smell baking even when I'm miles away," laughed Sven.

"Whatever it is that brings you, I am glad when you come. More glad than you know."

He motioned toward the oven. "That cake baking, is that for the governor Sunday or can common clay like myself taste it?"

"Let it but cool once it comes out, and you shall have some," promised Grandma. "Magrit made it."

"Oh no!" exclaimed Uncle Sven in mock horror. "I can't eat that cake. I'm sure to find a drawing pencil buried deep in the batter or perhaps a volume of Thomas Hardy."

He pinched me sharply as I set the coffee cups upon the cloth. "Did you know," he asked, "that the governor is a bachelor?"

"A middle-aged one," answered Grandma quickly, for she did not like too much teasing, "and not likely to exchange his freedom easily, as you should well know."

"Well, just remember," said Uncle Sven, tamping his pipe, "Aunt Gudrun is cooking dinner Sunday for a bachelor. A very important bachelor."

Uncle Sven went out into the evening's sharp frost and brought the Edison in to the library table in the living room, connected the big fluted black horn to the small walnut box, and showed me how to wind the handle and snap on a cylinder. "Every little movement has a meaning all its own," sang the seductive voice. Grandpa cocked his ear toward the phonograph and then sought his rocker again with a little sniff. Aunt Gudrun, who had been upstairs primping, came in looking fresh and beautiful. "After dinner I'm going up to Rekve's Store and shop for the party groceries," she explained. "Is supper ready?"

"I'm dishing it up now," I said from the kitchen doorway. "I'll do the dishes, too, Aunt Gudrun. If Grandpa doesn't mind, may I play the Edison while I'm doing them?"

"Far and I'll be down in the basement plucking chickens," said Grandma. "You may play it all you like."

The next morning Aunt Gudrun slipped out of bed before the household was awake, and I joined her in the chilly kitchen. "Shall I stay home and help you?"

"Grandma would not have you miss church for anything, not even for the governor," she said. "I suppose I ought to play the organ this morning, but Mrs. Wist can do it well enough. I sent word by one of the children."

Breakfast came and went, and the big oval pine table was soon cleared and enlarged by three leaves. Uncle Sven was commanded to bring down the three-tiered screen from an upstairs bedroom and place it in front of the kitchen range, already bursting with coal, aromas, and bubbling pots. "What good'll that screen do?" he scoffed. "Anybody but a fool would know what's on the other side."

"Just hush!" said Gudrun with good-natured weariness. "Two builders in our family, and we can't even have a dining room."

Grandma trudged down the stairway in her Sunday best. "I do not like this, Gudrun," she worried. "All this fuss and excitement and work for a dinner when you already have enough to do. We'll miss you at the organ," she said.

Gudrun swished us all out the back door. "You'll be late for church," she said, looking relieved as she shut the door upon us.

Our feet crackling in the frosty grass, we followed Grandpa up the lane. Grandma's arm trembled in my clasp. "Ole has always been like that," she said. "He leads his womenfolk down the pathway as though we were squaws following a chieftain."

"Do you remember the time in Tucson when he hustled us from the café to the streetcar stop when we had barely tasted our breakfast?" I laughed.

"I cannot remember the time when Ole was not in a hurry going somewhere, once he had made up his mind to go. But I have no criticism for him," she said quickly. "He is a fine man."

At the church door several blocks later, Grandpa waited for us at the foot of the stairs. "Half full already," he chided, "and you women walk as if you were out upon an afternoon stroll. Get in quickly now," he commanded, "lest even the Lord must wait upon you."

Grandma and Grandpa went forward near the front of the church and I slipped in beside a group of girls. Where was the governor? Where was he supposed to sit?

The Reverend Kjelland's handsome face peered from behind the altar and regarded the rapidly filling church with a worried glance. The choir in their black robes stirred restlessly. The Reverend Kjelland's face peered around the altar once again. He looked at the choir stall and the vacant bench before the organ. He looked at the crowded pews, and then he looked at me. I shifted nervously upon the hard oak bench. His face peered around the altar. His finger wagged. I looked in back of me. His finger wagged again. I blushed, and settled down in the seat. The robe swirling around his legs, he strode down the aisle, his face impatient and flushed. "What's the matter with Gudrun?" he said, hissing in my ear.

"She's cooking dinner," I replied.

"I want her here. We've got to fetch her," he said.

"Mrs. Wist is supposed to play."

"Gudrun plays the organ," he said. "Meet me at the back door. Hurry up!" he commanded.

I made my way quickly down the aisle, through the front door, through the long grasses at the side of the church. He stood waiting for me at the back beside his car, the wind blowing his robe in great billows. "Get in. Was she presentable when you left?"

"I think so," I lied, remembering the curlers in her hair and the beauty cream on her face.

"That's why I brought you along. To fetch her no matter how she looks. She'll have to get ready." He drove through the still Sunday streets in quiet fury. At the railroad crossing my head hit the top of the car. "She's just redheaded and stubborn enough," he said as he swirled the car around the dead end of our lane, "to refuse to come. If you have any trouble I'll be right in to fetch her."

"Yes," I assented meekly.

Gudrun met me at the front door. "What is it?"

"You have to play. He says you have to," I panted.

"Didn't Mrs. Wist come?"

"Not yet," I said.

"I thought so," said Gudrun. "I had a feeling this would happen, so I pulled the curlers out of my hair and powdered my face." She hustled me into the kitchen. "Start the potatoes and vegetables at twelve," she ordered. "Keep the fire moderately hot. Now where's my hat and coat?"

Aunt Gudrun's hand-etched crystal goblets sparkled on the linen tablecloth. The stove crackled cheerfully behind the cretonne camouflage which shut it from view. I sighed and went to work. I hoped the governor was fat and small and crabby. I hoped that when this Sunday was over Aunt Gudrun would thoroughly despise him. Even if he was a Republican.

When Uncle Thorvald's new black Buick came down the lane Aunt Gudrun was the first to alight. "Everything all right?" she asked, running in the back door. She tossed

me her hat and coat. "Thank goodness, politicians and preachers shake hands for hours. I'll have plenty of time," she said.

Bertina and Grandma shooed my sister Dode and me upstairs, where we lay across the bed sniffing the rich odors from the range below and talking about the morning's events. "What does the governor look like?" I asked.

"You'll see soon enough," replied Dode, "but I'd say he's awfully old." When we saw the preacher's car come flying down the lane we got off the bed and went into Grandma's room where the floor register gave us an unparalleled view of the room below.

"All I can see is his round head," I whispered to Dode, my nose pressed against the iron grating.

"Why, he's almost bald!" giggled Dode. "You couldn't see that in church," she explained.

"I used to watch Dr. Whitaker when he called on Aunt Gudrun," I whispered.

"Wonder whatever became of that?" asked Dode.

"Guess they just weren't in earnest," I explained importantly. By now Uncle Sven had spotted the heavenly eavesdroppers and was mugging horribly behind the governor's back and threatening to force us into spasms of giggles and the disgrace of discovery. When Aunt Gudrun announced dinner we went into the bedroom above the kitchen so that we could watch the grownups take their places at the table. "Mundy's children, and he's eating with them," I whispered.

"You know how Norwegians are," said Dode. "They'll always be nicer to someone that's going to grow up to be a man."

"I don't really care, do you?" I asked. "The second table's always better." But the vantage point was poor, here above the range; for we could see only the lower half of the table and what was left of the governor's menu keeping warm in the deep kettles toward the back of the stove. Aunt Gudrun's goblets tinkled, silver scratched against the plates. Suddenly there was a deep voice, heavy with Scandinavian inflections, and then a loud burst of laughter, followed by little volleys of trailing chuckles. "What did he say?" I asked. "I could hardly hear him."

"Bertina'll tell us," said Dode.

When the meal was over and the guests back in the living room, Bertina made a little island for us at one end of the table, and we sat down to Aunt Gudrun's fried chicken. Uncle Sven came in from the living room. "That's over," he said. "You heard what the governor said, didn't you, Bertina?"

"What did he say?" asked Emily. "We heard you all laughing."

"*Saw* us, you mean," corrected Uncle Sven good-naturedly. "The governor said," repeated Uncle Sven, "that every morning when he awakened and looked over to find the pillow beside his vacant, with no long-haired Eve beside him, he thanked the Lord for a new free day."

I had always been a Republican ever since I had been big enough to sit on Grandpa's knees and agree heartily with everything he supported, even his politics; but now I knew that not only would I remain a Republican, but if that plump, elderly bachelor sitting on the other side of our kitchen door should ever run for office when I was old enough to vote, he had my vote already.

23

The Centennial   Winter had surrendered quietly at last. The first pasqueflowers bloomed in the pasture north of the railroad tracks. On Easter morning the meadow lark, perched on a rail at the corner of the fence, sang his song of faith above the dark, melting snows.

When the school year was over the plump football coach passed Mamie and me in algebra, not because of our personal achievement but because passing us was easier than explaining our failure. Miss Bauer picked up her English notes and went back to Minnesota for a summer's vacation, but not without leaving an abiding sense of beauty in our memories. For with this small, gentle teacher we had stormed the citadels of power with Sir Walter Scott; we had heard the clash of arms and the rumble of chariots on the plains of Troy. "Write me this summer," she had said; and she would never know how many letters I had torn up to start again; for the idols of one's youth are like the gods of old.

So the two-story brick schoolhouse drowsed in the summer sun and children were home again; and the vacant lots, lush with ambitious grass, rang to the calls of "Duck on the rock" and "Your turn next."

Grandpa climbed a ladder and painted the steep little house again. Gudrun scratched in her flower beds, while the long evening shadows stretched across the lawn and reached the tender corn plants north of the willow grove. Grandma sat in a rocker near the back steps, her hands strangely idle and her eyes on the twilight vault of sky. A block away the frogs in the big slough by the state highway set up their chorus of water-choked gurgling. And in the cobbled house beside the slough old Mrs. Schwantz hobbled back and forth between the chicken house and the sagging red barn, singing Baptist hymns in a quaking, off-key voice. The crimson-streaked western sky paled; the evening star glinted richly through the rustling cottonwood leaves.

Grandpa put away his buckets, and Gudrun washed the black loamy soil off her hands in a bucket drawn from the rain barrel beside the chicken house. I walked in with Grandma, who stirred the slumbering lignite flames into bursting flares, added a shovel of coal, and put the coffee-pot on the front of the stove. From the shelf below the clock she took down the book of family devotions.

"You read tonight," suggested Grandpa, sighing with weariness after the day's painting. Gudrun fingered the edge of the white tablecloth with restless fingers. As Grandma began to read the evening's devotions a moth darted out of the back entry and threw its fluttering wings against the shaded light bulb hanging from the ceiling. A cricket behind the stove struck a rasping note, held onto it, grew silent, and rasped again. The moth circled the orbit of its new-found sun in rapturous, narrowing flights, struck sharply against the swinging light, and fell dying to the floor. Grandma paused.

"Are you listening, Magrit?" she asked. "Or do you learn your lessons from the moth?"

"I'm listening," I said.

When the reading was over Grandma took sugar cookies
out of the stone crock on the pantry floor, and Gudrun

set the coffee cups upon the table. "Are you all really going to Minneapolis?" I asked.

"I cannot decide," said Grandma.

Grandpa shook his head. "*Du maa*, you must," he said. "For years you have hoarded your wealth, and there must come a time when you are willing to spend it." We laughed, for well we knew about Grandma's birthday checks, money arriving from Uncle Henry, a dollar for every year she had lived.

"You get paid for growing old!" I teased.

"And well one might!" exclaimed Grandma. "It is not easy to watch the diminishing of one's powers when the need for strength still remains."

"Oh, *Mor!*" scolded Gudrun. "All we want of you is to have you with us. Margaret and I shall keep house this summer, and in the fall Ragna or her sister will be back to help us."

"It's strange," twinkled Grandpa, "how fast the little wealth I can put my hands on disappears; but Guro here grows ever richer and puts her little hoard away."

"I need so little!" exclaimed Grandma. "Clothes I possess for the rest of my living days. What do I need beyond my offering to the church on Sunday and thread and wool and patches of linen for my sewing to make small gifts throughout the year?"

"If you feel well enough," insisted Grandpa, "I think all three of us should go to the Centennial in Minneapolis."

"What is it for, *Bestefar?*"

"The landing of the first Norwegian immigrants upon the soil of North America," he said. "They took a small sailing vessel and crossed the stormy Atlantic in ten weeks' time. You *must* go, Guro," he finished earnestly. "For Henry will be there from Tucson, and we shall see many whom we knew from our years in Wisconsin and Minnesota."

"Who'll stay with Magrit?" she asked.

"Bertina'll come down," said Aunt Gudrun. "They'll have a good time keeping house and visiting."

"Well, I'll go," conceded Grandma, "but only because I'll have some time with Henry there."

So when the coffee train whistled across the prairies on a cloudless afternoon they all got on, Grandpa in his new suit and Grandma with a new blue summer coat and a straw hat entwined with bachelor buttons. I waved good-by with a glad but lonely heart, for I was old enough to understand that this was for them a journey of joy, and might even be their last.

In the freshly painted house Bertina and I, each possessing a like energy and determination, dragged the very insides of the house outdoors or into the basement to be washed. Aunt Tina's old Wonder-Washer, which now spent its old age with us and needed only a willing and tireless hand upon a lever to agitate the clothes back and forth, hummed its accompaniment to our optimistic endeavors. Dally also pulled old cookbooks from the pantry cupboard and dreamed up cookies rich with fillings, while I took Aunt Gudrun's red furniture polish and rubbed the old library table and the piano and bookcase into the flush of youth.

"When I get married, Dally," I confided, "I'm going to 232 scrub and clean and polish all day long!"

Bertina turned a thoughtful glance my way. "I don't think I'll ever get married!" she sighed. "I'm twenty already, and if my affair with Ronnie is a sign of my success with men, I'll never have a house of my own!"

"What's the matter, Dally?" I cried, snuggling up to my sister.

She wiped her floury hands upon the back of her apron. "Maybe I'm to blame, or maybe it's Aunt Tina," she said honestly. "I know she means well, but she's so strict about everything I do, she scares Ronnie away. If we come home and sit on the porch in the moonlight she calls for me to come in. If I entertain him in the house she's in and out of the living room, eying him as though he might pounce on me at any moment." She turned back to the floured board, patted the cooky dough, and brushed the rolling pin back and forth.

"Do you know, Mugs, what I'll do?" she asked thoughtfully. "Aunt Tina and Uncle Thorvald and all of us are going to the north farm on Sunday to look over the crop. Aunt Tina says we'll call on the Sturvesons too. But I'll stay home and have Ronnie over for supper that evening!"

"Do you think you dare?" I asked hopefully.

"Well, why not?" she asked. "If I'm old enough to have gone to college and to be teaching school, I'm old enough to entertain a man."

So on Sunday Bertina, bright-eyed and flushed, came down to rifle the chicken coop for eggs. "I'm going to make a cheese soufflé," she confided. "Aunt Tina wonders if you'd like to ride along with them. She thinks I'm silly staying home on such a lovely day."

"I'll stay home," I said, "and she'll think you have to stay to keep an eye on me."

"Just so you're not staying home to keep an eye on me!" she teased.

"I'll be down here every minute," I protested, a little hurt over her teasing. "I'm going to dust all the furniture in the whole house again, 'cause the family'll be back in the morning." But when I got as far as my room above the willow grove I sat at the low window and imagined it was I making a soufflé in the kitchen below, instead of Dally up at Aunt Tina's. And the man who stood beside the range and talked with me was tall and blue-eyed like Grandpa in his uniform of the Norwegian army, in the picture Grandma had tucked away. Why did it take so long to grow up? I wondered.

When Dally came running through the cornfield it was twilight. "I had a wonderful time, and so did Ronnie!" she said. "I got the dishes done and put away, and Ronnie helped me, and afterward he played his violin for me."

We turned the lights off downstairs and went up to bed. "Was that sort of dishonest, Dally? What you did, having him for supper without telling Aunt Tina?"

Dally stood at Aunt Gudrun's dresser, her lace-trimmed nightgown falling gracefully from her shoulders and clinging seductively to her firm bosom. She drew a comb slowly through her satin-brown hair. "I don't think so," she said, giving the subject some thought. "I don't think so because we felt so right about being together like that, eating and laughing and talking. More right about it than at other times when we're being watched and criticized."

234   I snuggled down into the sheets that smelled freshly of

sun and wind and prairie. "Dally," I said, "when that nightgown gets awfully worn and you don't want it any more, could I please have it?"

Dally snapped off the light and chuckled warmly. "Silly!" she laughed. "You can have it when it's only a teensy bit worn!"

When the morning train had left them on the depot platform and Uncle Thorvald's Buick brought them home, Grandpa talked happily of those he had met and often chuckled over past events; but Grandma climbed the stairs to their bedroom and lay quietly, with a psalm book beside her or a little church paper. "Read to me," she said; and I read wondrously sad tales of men lost at sea or little ser-monettes expounding the virtue of a Christ-directed life.

Summer moved toward autumn, and still Grandma had to rest more than was her wont. And as she grew more frail her veined hands slid surreptitiously across the hard dome of her stomach. "I am eighty-three," she said, always with a gentle laugh, "and yet I feel as one carrying a child."

I laid aside the paper from which I had been reading. "Is it true, *Bestemor*, that I killed my mother in order to be born?"

"Who told you that?"

"I've heard them talk," I said.

"Always there must be talk," said Grandma, rising slowly and sitting on the edge of the bed. "I think if a woman finds the gates of paradise barred to her it will not be the deeds she did or failed to do, but it will be her tongue that bars her entrance. How many a woman," she exclaimed, "would have been better off had she been un-

able to speak at all, and how many of her loved ones might

have been spared a very *helvede*, a very hell upon this earth!" She took my arm and teetered to her feet. "Ole will want his afternoon coffee," she said.

Downstairs, when the coffee dishes had been set upon the table, Grandma sat down in the rocker. "Your mother did die several hours after your birth," she said. "But you did not ask admittance to this earth; and even had you, she would have bid you welcome, no matter what the cost."

"But I have heard Aunt Tina and Gudrun say it was a tragedy for her to have had five children!"

"*Ja vist?*" said Grandma with some asperity. "And who are they to judge the private affairs of another, even a sister?"

"They do not like my father," I pursued, driven to find the truth which had been a living torment to my childhood.

"It was only that they could not forgive your father's taking her away from the safety and security they had found in Minneapolis to the unbroken plains where there was neither help nor doctor for sudden childbirth." She sighed and stroked the wrinkled hand lying upon the arm of the chair.

"And afterward, didn't our father want us?"

"I'm sure he did," she said; "but you were all so small, how should he have cared for you? A neighbor woman from across the hills came and bore you to her home and cared for you and would have kept you except that we could not part with you nor any. We thought it best to keep them all within the family fold. Mistakes we've made, for erring humans are we all." She rose to take the coffeepot off the stove. "*Nei vist!*" she exclaimed. "Look down the path, but is that not Grandma Rekve and Janice's mother?"

Grandma stroked her hair with shaking hands. "Go fetch my Hardanger cloth," she said, "and the blue luncheon plates from the upper shelf in the cupboard. Run quickly, and make the table pretty while I meet them at the door."

When Grandpa stomped the garden soil off his feet at the back door I told him there was company for coffee. He stroked his fine mustache, and his eyes twinkled with laughter. "In that case I shall have my cup of coffee outdoors," he said. "A man could choke over the great talk and the small food that one gets when women get together for afternoon coffee."

Grandma made little forays into the kitchen to check on my progress. "I should have baked," sighed Grandma, "instead of lying upon my back looking at the ceiling."

But when I called them in, Aunt Gudrun's yellow nasturtiums filled the blue crock in the center of the table. Sunday's cake and Bertina's rich, filled cookies lay upon plates. And Grandma Rekve, whose own pastries were light enough to take wing, seemed not to notice that Grandma's cake was slightly stale. Mrs. Saylor said, "Janice would have come, but she's taking her music lessons today. You'll see a lot of each other when school begins."

When the cottonwood shadows rippled across the eaves and danced upon the lawn they took their leave, Grandma Rekve straight and thin, her gray-black hair drawn back in neat waves to a knot at the nape of her neck. "What a 237 remarkable woman Uncle Thorvald's mother is!" remarked

Grandma later. "She is like the best of apples, tart but never sharp, with all her wisdom and reading." Grandma stirred the slumbering coals to life. "It disturbs Mrs. Saylor that you often walk to school with Nannie Tweiler."

"But why? What did she say?"

"Among the women in town there is talk that Nannie and some of the high school girls see more of boys than might be wise."

"Nannie goes out with boys, but I've never heard her say an evil thing!" I defended hotly.

"Then walk with Nannie when the occasion arises," said Grandma; "for more harm can be done by unkindness to a human soul than by knowledge." She drew a knotted hand against her wrinkled brow. "Indeed, I am too old, too much of another time, to advise and admonish the young of today. But this I can tell you, that women who start talk of matters between men and women often have something to conceal themselves. They talk most loud who conceal the murmurings of their own conscience. I am not talking now of Janice's mother, for she is a fine and honest woman; but this I know, even with my having grown old and stupid, that there are good mothers in this town who are quick with their tongues about the young, but conceived themselves before their marriage vows." She glanced quickly at my shocked face.

"I do not mean to frighten you, but who will talk of such things when I am gone? Time runs through my fingers like sand in the sea. I am of the old country, where even the young saw birth and death, and knew the stuff of which our stormy lives are made."

238   The red peelings from the potato in my hand spiraled

down from the paring knife like the swirls from Grandpa's carpenter plane. "*Bestemor*," I said, "why does Aunt Tina distrust Bertina when she is in love?"

"I could not know with certainty," she replied. "But if you borrowed two fine china plates from a neighbor, the plates you borrowed you would wash and wipe with extra care, lest you harm them before their return. So it is with Christina, who is strict even with herself, and regards her sister's children as a trust beyond the grave."

"People are all mixed up, *Bestemor!*" I cried. "Must it always be this way?"

She set the coffee grinder down upon the table beside her. "Perhaps not," she said. "Have I not always said it is not easy to be young?"

24

"Behold a Host"[1]   It was 1925. It was the year of the long Indian summer. The shocked grain had disappeared into the maws of rumbling threshing machines, and stubble fields glinted richly in the warm sun. In the fields of shocked corn, birds, poised for their long flight southward, gleaned the leavings, flung themselves upward, and floated darkly against the bright sky.

At the Saturday morning breakfast table I sat with my head resting in cupped palms. "The first time I saw your grandfather," remarked *Bestemor*, "he was nursing at his mother's breast."

I giggled. Grandma looked at me through her bifocals. "Is that so funny?" she asked. "I was only four, and he was

239   [1]*The Lutheran Hymnary*, p. 528.

but a baby. Is that not how babies have always taken nourishment?"

"I was not laughing at that, *Bestemor!*" I explained. "Only at the idea of Grandpa, now so tall, being only a baby, and you toddling about watching him!"

"Time, as you shall see, changes us all." She pointed at the geometric designs on the linoleum floor, where a ray of sunlight, escaping from banked clouds, lighted a patch of floor. "How much I have found to give me joy!" she exclaimed. "Since I was a baby I have exulted over a patch of sunlight upon a kitchen floor. In Norway where the scrubbed wood shone like stubble fields, in Wisconsin with the children playing on the rag rugs upon a clean floor—here in Dakota. Always have I had a sudden lift of heart with the sun's quick shining. People may be unkind, even our own loved ones fail to understand, but sunlight, bird song, and the quiet coming of night are the merciful reminders of the hovering spirit of God." I sat quietly in thought.

Then I asked, "Didn't you feel strange marrying a man younger than yourself?"

"Was I not young myself?" she countered. "And when you love do you sit and count the spanning years?" She smiled. "When the wedding bells are about to ring, I promise you that you will have other thoughts, and not of the years that separate. Unless," she finished, "you are foolish enough to marry an old man."

"Tell me about other romances in the family!" I begged.

"This is the day you read for the minister," she reminded, "and there are dishes to do and the house to put 240 to rights for Sunday."

"But I'll fly about the house soon. You'll see!" I begged.

"*Ja, tiden er haer.* The time is here," she said. "How fast the years run between the cradle and girlhood, and then even faster to the grave," she finished soberly.

"How did my mother meet—my father?" I finished bashfully. Even after all these years it was difficult to link their names together. But there was an urgency now to probe at mysteries, an urgency I did not fully understand myself, to draw Grandma out on many subjects.

"They met after we came from Norway," she said. "Your father's people were known to ours—even remotely related. They had been in America a generation before us, and grew tobacco and even had a cigar factory, where your Uncle Henry found his first employment."

"Did my mother love my father?" I asked.

"*Forvetenheit!* Such curiosity!" scorned Grandma. "Who can probe the hearts of youth? Let us suppose she did!"

"But you once told me she was loved by a young red-haired minister."

"Indeed?" she asked. "When one has a memory like yours that never forgets, must you sit and question an old one like me? *Morgenstund har guld i Mund,*" she quoted. "Morning hours carry gold in their mouths, so let us not foolishly spend them."

"But I'll do the work, all of it, as I promised. It is only that it is so cozy to sit and talk. I am in school all week, and I grow lonesome for the hours we used to sit and chat."

"*Javel,* all right," she conceded. "These days I am not altogether loath to sit and let younger feet run my errands."

"Did my mother *want* to marry my father?" I persisted.

"Who knows the sudden turnings of a girl's heart?" she said. "We were happy at the match, for we owed your father's people much, since they had befriended us in a new and strange land." I finished stacking the plates and thought deeply of the stranger who had been my mother, of her youth and her shorter married years.

"How beautifully your mother sewed!" exclaimed Grandma. "She was an artist with her needle. It was her trade—dressmaking—before she married, as millinery was your Aunt Christina's."

"Did Aunt Christina have a millinery store here before she married Uncle Thorvald?"

"She *had* been in millinery," said Grandma, "but when she married Thorvald she was a bookkeeper in the Rekve Store." She took up her mending basket.

"Is it true that Uncle Thorvald once courted Aunt Gudrun?"

"One must take care," laughed Grandma, settling down into her rocker, "how one talks before you, for nothing is ever lost."

"Years ago you told me that yourself!" I chided, pumping water to pour into the reservoir of the range.

"Well, perhaps I did," she conceded. "I remember once we wondered which of my two girls it would be. Gudrun was like a rippling brook, quick and hard to follow; but Tina was a quiet stream, deep and steady. And when a man fishes for a wife, though he may cast about in a running stream, it is often in the deep and quiet pool where he lands his fish." I laughed. "But hasten with your work," she entreated, "for in these days of *Høstfred,* autumn

242

peace, school children should have many outside hours."

And still winter bided its time. The cottonwoods and elms and willows stood deep in drifting amber and wine leaves. In the morning hoarfrost jeweled the ground but soon melted in the gentle sun. Grandpa took down the window screens, dusted off the storm windows to have me wash them, and stacked them in readiness at the back of the house.

Hurrying home from school one crisp November afternoon, I found Grandma in the living room, with the sun a golden shaft of light at her feet. "How beautiful you look!" I exclaimed, tossing my books upon the library table. "I hurried home to be of help."

"That's good. But tonight we need not concern ourselves with cooking supper. For Selma and Ronald have been out hunting, and Aunt Tina is cooking prairie chicken for us all." She put the mending basket on the floor beside her. "Mrs. Tweiler sent over doughnuts. We have had our coffee, but there is food for you on the kitchen table."

"You have changed so lately, *Bestemor!*" I exclaimed, settling down on the settee above the furnace register, a doughnut in my hand, the hot air from the furnace blowing out my Russian plaid skirt.

"*Ja, saa?*" she asked. "Is that so?"

"If I wished to paint a picture of peace, it would be you, *Bestemor,*" I said, studying the serene white face below its broad and wrinkled brow.

"*Merkvaerdig,* remarkable that you should notice it," she said, "for I have these past months, and these past
243 weeks in particular, felt a peace I have never known be-

fore. The voices of the long-dim past sound pleasantly in my ears; and the stirrings in my memory recall scenes I'd long forgotten. But that is not all," she added gently, "but even more wonderful—the eternal arms seem to welcome me; and in my quiet moments in this peaceful, sunlit room I feel surrounded by ministering spirits from above." She spoke so earnestly, so quietly, that when she said no more I could not speak either. "I do not mean to frighten you," she said at last, "but I am glad that my days will soon have their ending, and that heaven sends down its shaft of light to guide us upward, so that we need not walk in darkness. But have you not lessons to do," she suggested gently, "so that you may be free to enjoy the evening at Aunt Tina's?"

There had never been anything about a chicken I liked: not the excited, futile squawkings of Aunt Gudrun's Plymouth Rocks in the pen under the cottonwoods, nor even the platters of crusty fried chicken so often on the table for Sunday dinner. So I knew from long experience that I should like even less the wild, sharp flavor of prairie chicken and wild pheasant; but a dinner at Aunt Tina's was always something. It was the marriage of good cooking and a pleasant household. When the dishes had been scraped, stacked, washed, and dried, my sister Dode sat down at the piano and played her latest music. Aunt Gudrun rocked happily, Grandpa nodded in his chair, Grandma sat in the dining-room doorway, her hands folded quietly on her lap. Mundy, skirmishing lightly with his fox terrier, lay upon his stomach on the living-room rug. But the faces of Aunt Tina and Uncle Thorvald were 244 alive with pride.

"When she goes to college next year," Uncle remarked, "I hope she specializes in music."

"I'm sure she will," remarked Aunt Gudrun as though Dode were not there—a habit the family had, seeming to feel they could be more articulate about us than we ourselves.

"But I must go," said Grandma finally. "I cannot stay for coffee when the rest come over later"—meaning Selma, Ronald, and their three next door.

"I'll walk home with you," I said.

Outside the rising moon threw sharply etched shadows upon the frosty ground. The air was brittle and clear. When we left the gate at the back of Uncle Thorvald's yard and walked upon the frozen, rutted path in the denuded cornfield, Grandma's slender arm rested heavily upon my own. "I am sorry to be so slow," she said.

"I'd rather be out here in this clear moonlight than anywhere else," I said, listening to the bark of a farm dog a half mile away.

"How often your young feet have guided me across this field at night! We took you in when even to breathe was a miracle, you were so far gone with whooping cough," she said, "and now that you are grown, your feet are here to guide my shuffling steps." She stopped to catch her breath and looked about the moon-washed fields with interest. "And I believe surely," she went on quietly, "that the young who pause to help the old upon their paths will themselves be helped someday. You will see," she said.

When I had snapped the lights on in the house and banked the furnace and coaxed the kitchen fire to life, she
245 turned to me and said, "Run back up to Aunt Tina's, if

you are not afraid to cross the field alone, and have your fun with those of your age."

"I don't like to leave you alone," I remonstrated.

"Did I not tell you just this afternoon that I am never alone? Run now, that I may rest."

On a Saturday early in December we awoke to find the frost glinting upon every shrub and branch, and a quiet, deep snowfall lay upon the fields. Uncle Sven coaxed Grandma out to the side of the house at noon to take a picture in the sparkling sunlight. "Can it be done quickly?" she begged. "I am so weak and swollen with pain, I cannot stand for long, even on such a pleasant winter's day." She wore her blue serge dress trimmed with scalloped braiding, and her folded arms pressed against her aching stomach

"I'll hurry it," whispered Uncle Sven. But Grandma's ears were keen, with eighty-three years' practice. "Do that," she said, "for I but disfigure a beautiful landscape."

As dusk deepened she said with wonder, "So sharp is the raging in my stomach, I cannot even climb the stairs." So Aunt Gudrun pulled off the bedspread in the spare bedroom downstairs, and Grandma lay down, sick with exhaustion. Yet she looked up with surprise to see the doctor's husky form within the doorway. He examined her patiently and gently.

"I'll check further," he said, coming later into the kitchen, "but I am positive it is cancer. She will never get up again, and all we can do is try to make her comfortable. Be thankful," he said in his gruff, kind way to Grandpa and Aunt Gudrun, "that she knows she will never leave her bed. Her mind is settled on that score." When he left, Grandpa got up from her rocker beside the fire and went

in to her.

December moved on, with night encroaching upon snow-filled days. We arose by artificial light; often we studied by light in schoolrooms filled with the wonder and discouragement of learning; and we turned on the lamps in the little house by the willows when it was but coffee time.

Drawn and pale and smiling, Grandma reached for my hand before I left for school, and smiled her quiet welcome upon my return. Ragna came in from the country; and Uncle Olaf and his gentle wife rode in on snowy roads and spent some quiet hours in the bedroom. One evening Aunt Gudrun said, "Henry will be here from Tucson as soon as he can make it. He insists upon a nurse, and I am glad, for I have felt all along she must need one."

So Dr. Whitaker met the coffee train on a gray afternoon and came in to the house with a dimpled, red-haired nurse who might have been one of Grandpa's own daughters, so tall she was and fair and smiling. She put up a cot in the living room, laughed at our brave and foolish jokes, and cared tenderly for the wasting form lying within the sound of our voices. Grandpa, who always liked pretty women, gave her his gentle, shy smile and settled down beside the stove in Grandma's rocker and once again began to read.

"I'm Scotch," said Laura MacIntosh, "but I feel at home with all of you." Grandpa looked up from his book and said, "Scotland is only a handclasp away from the fjords of Norway, and the Vikings often stole their maidens from your land." They laughed; and a sense of peace was again in the kitchen. Yet it was never lonelier in the house than that night, for Grandpa shuffled up the stairway and went to bed alone, as he was to do for the rest of his life.

When Grandma's first-born came on a morning train, she had a lift of spirit; for among them all, Uncle Henry was most like her, firm, gentle, and comprehending. "He did not have to come," she said, "from so far away." But there was a huge pride in her saying it, and when he left, so did some of her spirit.

"Geometry isn't so hard!" declared Miss MacIntosh. "Let me help you." She brushed aside the crumbs upon the table, bent her shining head above my figures, and a little sail of light winked suddenly upon the dark seas of learning.

January came—cold, clear, and sunny, with the snow banked in huge wind-driven swirls around the house.

"What have we here?" asked Grandma, staring at my strange clothes as I started out for school.

"It's tacky day, *Bestemor*," I said. "But if you would rather, I'll take these silly clothes off, for I don't feel like that at all. I don't even want to go to school. I want to stay at home!" I cried.

"So they have told you," she said. "I know the end is near, for they put me to sleep too often. I would rather bear more pain than lose these hours in my home. I had the nurse call you," she said in a husky, whispering voice, "because I want to ask one thing of you. I know your fear of death, and remember how it was with you when Grandpa Rekve died: I would not have you feel that way now," she said, her hand seeking mine across the coverlet.

"I would not have you feel that way now, for it is not in keeping with what I have taught you." Her thin, veined hand rested lightly in mine. "When I am gone," she said, "and they have put this aching body upon its final bed, promise that you will come in and look at me, if only for a moment. You will see that this old body whose hand stroked away your childish griefs and cared for you as a mother would has no harm in it nor danger to your peace."

When I began to weep she silenced me. "I am not strong enough to bear much more, so go to school and do not grieve; but remember well the lessons I have taught you so that the peace of God may go with you into eternity."

We were up at Aunt Tina's late that afternoon when the minister walked across the high-banked snow and in the back door. "She is gone, girls," he said. Aunt Gudrun was at his side. I flung myself into her arms. He stood beside us for a moment, and then he said, "She died as she lived, in peace with all, so there is nothing much I can say except that I share your loss with all of you."

When he left Aunt Tina said, "I can't forget the look of joy upon her face."

"Nor how she called out a greeting when her spirit fled," said Aunt Gudrun.

And so I found that it was as *Bestemor* had said: the folded hands bore me no harm, nor did the peaceful shining face seem cold or frightening. In the quiet little church the choir sang her favorite hymn in Norwegian:

"Behold a host arrayed in white,
  Like thousand snow-clad mountains bright."

But parting cut like a sharpened knife, and grief lay like a heavy stone upon the spirit. It was at Aunt Selma's later in the day, when she had fed us and tried to talk away the worst of the gloom, that the snowflakes began to fall, swirling in spirals to the heavy fir branches separating the two Rekve houses. I wanted to cry out in pain at the thought of Grandma laid to rest alone under the drifting snow.

It was then I saw Grandpa start down across Uncle Thorvald's yard to the back gate, his head bent against the rising wind, his steps searching the obliterated path across the field. "I'm going with *Bestefar*," I called to Aunt Gudrun as I found my wraps.

When I caught up with him frosty tears glistened on his cheeks. "I'm going down to the house, *Bestefar!*" I called. He only nodded. But after we had built up the banked fires and the kettle upon the stove began to sing, it was almost as if *Bestemor* had not gone at all. Her book of daily devotions lay upon the shelf under the ticking wall clock, her silver knitting needles glinted from the woven sewing basket pushed halfway under the settee; and her brown-checked homespun shawl lay folded upon the foot of the homemade sofa.

"None will ever know how I feel this day," said Grandpa. I sat down upon the sofa and put my arms around him.

25

The Open Door   The little blue pamphlet sailed to the middle of the bed in the room I shared with Aunt Gudrun. "Here is something for you to read," she said, leaving the room to descend the stairway.

I finished running a comb through my hair, went over

to the bed, and leafed through the booklet. After scanning several pages of flowery prose, I concluded that I had been now apprised—thanks to the generosity of a free bulletin—of the fact I stood at the place in life where "the brook and river meet."

"Hurry! Hurry!" called Aunt Gudrun up the stair well. "You'll be late for school. I'm going now," she finished, "but don't forget to meet me in the store after school tonight so we can pick out your confirmation dress."

"I'm ready," I called, still scanning pages in the little brochure. "Shoulders back, head high, stretch to the full stature of your unfolding womanhood," I read. I glanced at the ticking alarm clock on top of the oak dresser and thrust the pamphlet hastily under a pillow on the bed.

A minute or so later I caught up with my sister Emily, waiting for me on the corner beyond the old Rekve livery stable. She stood there slim and straight, her red hair curling becomingly under the brim of her tam-o'-shanter. "Do you know what Aunt Gudrun gave me this morning?" I asked, matching my steps with hers.

"No, what?" she asked dreamily.

"A pamphlet," I laughed. "A pamphlet on the facts of life."

"What's it all about?"

"I haven't had a chance to read much yet, but I'll pass it on to you soon." Out of the corner of my eye I studied my sister—now a senior—and decided that I was perhaps presumptuous to believe that anyone ready to graduate from high school needed coaching on any subject, especially when *she* had been smart enough to take solid geometry and trigonometry as electives. "Does Aunt Tina ever talk to you about—things?" I asked.

"You know Aunt Tina," she said. "There are some things she just doesn't talk about."

"I know," I said. "I'm glad I had Grandma, because Grandma'd answer questions."

"I suppose she felt you were at a disadvantage," said Dode kindly, "being raised by someone who's never married." A silence fell, as it often did these months after Grandma's funeral. I missed her at every turn: her step on the stairway, the creak of her rocking chair, the gentle sighs she breathed when she was lost in thought—yet what was this hovering sense of closeness that had come out of the first chaos of pain to steal into mind and heart like a warning dream half remembered, like a voice dimly heard?

"Uncle says he has some nice white dresses in for confirmation," remarked Dode as we swung open the back door of the Rekve Store to pass through the building as we always did on our way to school.

"I'm meeting Aunt Gudrun here tonight to pick mine out," I said. Solveig slipped off a dry goods counter where she had been sitting and joined us, her lustrous brown eyes alive with smoldering fires, her long shining brown hair caught loosely in a ribbon at her neck.

"I wish I was getting confirmed with you and Janice, Mugs," she said.

Outside we linked our arms together and went down Main Street, past the pool hall where the fat Dutch proprietor sat near the dusty window and regarded us sluggishly, to wink slowly as he came into range of our peripheral vision. "Gee, his winks used to worry me!" I laughed,

tossing my head back to indicate the Hollander who had sat there and watched our comings and goings since our first days of school.

"I know," laughed Dode. "That's probably why he winks." The school bell began to ring, vibrating in the old tower on top of the red brick building. We scurried down the mud-splattered sidewalk.

Late that afternoon Aunt Gudrun and I were crowded into a dressing room in the Rekve Store. "Now don't let me influence you," she said, "but that's the dress you should have." I regarded my image in the long mirror.

"I like the dress," I admitted quickly, studying the white crepe de chine with its simple rounded collar, the banded waist, and the flowing skirt, "but do I have to wear a corset? Why? Why?"

"You read the pamphlet, didn't you?"

"Well, yes, part of it," I admitted.

"All right. Now you know you're growing up."

"I knew that already, Aunt Gudrun," I said. "But why do I have to wear a corset? It makes me feel like my insides are crammed into a barrel!"

Aunt Gudrun rose to her full height. "Why do you suppose I have kept my figure? I'll tell you why, because I never let myself get careless." She skimmed over me with a trace of disgust in her expression. "Now straighten up and get the hair out of your eyes."

"All this stuff you're doing to me only makes me feel worse!" I rebelled.

"What do you mean?"

"Oh, these horrid horn-rimmed glasses and this fence 254 around my stomach. If that's growing up I don't like it!"

"Well, I still maintain a figure doesn't just come to a woman. You have to work for it like anything else you get."

The saleswoman peered around the door. "We'll take the dress and the corset, Clara," emphasized Aunt Gudrun.

In the shoe department Uncle Thorvald was waiting for us. "The shoes are to be a gift from Aunt Tina and me," he said, waving us to the leather chairs waiting stiffly in a row. I began to protest his generosity. Aunt Gudrun scowled.

"Thank you, Thorvald," she said pleasantly. "Did the white silk stockings come in?"

"Not yet, Gudrun, but we expect our shipment of hosiery any day." Uncle took his sliding foot measure and slipped it under my foot. "We'll take a half size larger," he mused, scanning the low shelves. "I've always sold children shoes that way and I always will. Something to grow on, I say."

I looked at my outthrust foot in horror. "Please don't let him sell me something as long as snowshoes, Aunt Gudrun!" I whispered.

"Anything wrong?" asked Uncle, coming forward with a shoebox.

Aunt Gudrun shook her head at me. "Nothing, Uncle," I said.

He slipped a white kidskin pump from the box. "Try this on," he said, extending the shoe with a shoehorn placed in the heel. As easily as a boat launched into deep water, the shoe slipped on.

"They're beautiful, Uncle," I said as he straightened up and regarded my expression with a hugely satisfied smile.

"Well?" invited Uncle.

"They are a little big," I suggested timidly, shifting my toes experimentally from side to side.

"Nonsense!" exclaimed Uncle, wriggling his cigar from the left side of his face to the right. "You measure five and a half, and you get a half to grow on."

"But my feet won't grow any more!" I exclaimed.

"How are you going to stop them?" taunted Aunt Gudrun dryly.

"I won't let them," I said, feeling dispirited, awkward in a way that only an adolescent can.

"Now I don't want to influence you," said Aunt Gudrun, "but these shoes will be perfect with your white confirmation dress. Yes, these will be fine, Thorvald," she finished with a big smile, nudging one of my corset ribs.

"Yes, thank you, Uncle," I said. "They are beautiful, Uncle," I continued, suffocated with embarrassment over his largess and the little imp of a voice that whispered to me, "It's these shoes or none. Don't you know that?" Uncle unrolled brown wrapping paper and expertly wrapped the box.

He handed the shoes to me with a grinning flourish. "Thanks again," I said. "I'll drop by Aunt Tina's and thank her too."

"That'll be fine," said Uncle. "We're proud to do it, proud that you're a young lady now ready for confirmation." He turned to Aunt Gudrun. "Anything I can do for you?" he asked.

They moved down the aisle. "She'll like them," said Uncle Thorvald in a conspiratorial voice. "Matter of fact it's the only one of last summer's stock we had in her size. Too early for summer shoes, you know."

Down in the house beside the willow grove I stood in our bedroom trying on the new white dress (*sans* corset) and mugging pleasantly before the mirror. Why did Aunt Gudrun have to concentrate on such purely unpleasant things as posture, corsets, hair in the eyes when everyone— with the exception of the family—always pointed out what a lovely complexion I had? So far as our silent Scandi- navians were concerned, I thought with rebelliousness, I might as well be wearing snakeskins over my bones instead of a milk-and-roses complexion.

I slipped the dress over my head, stroked the silky ma- terial, and hung it carefully in the clothes closet. In the kitchen Ragna was shaking down the coals in the range, and I heard Grandpa's cane tap-tap-tapping on the side- walk below my room. Poor *Bestefar*, I thought—he had slowed down since Grandma's death, and had even taken to his bed for a while. Perhaps with summer's coming the roses would be back in his cheeks and his step would again be firm. His spirit was like a boat with one oar, circling futilely on a lake of loneliness.

Perhaps *he* could answer a question that had been per- plexing me lately. I stacked my books upon the writing desk, with Thomas Hardy's *Return of the Native* under the pile, and skipped down the stairway.

"*Du er heim?*" he asked as I entered the living room. "You are home? It was so still here, with only Ragna in the kitchen, I thought I was alone, as I often am these days."

"I'm so busy, *Bestefar*, with all my lessons and getting ready for confirmation next Sunday."

"*Ja*," he said with a little nod of his head, "the young are always busy, but the old have time to sit and think."

"*Bestefar*," I began, slipping to the arm of his chair and wishing I were small enough again to sit on his lap as I used to, "how serious are the vows of confirmation?"

"What do you mean? Any vow is not to be taken lightly. Particularly one made to God Almighty."

"I have to renounce the Devil, the world, and the flesh," I said soberly. "Who can do anything as big as that, *Bestefar*?"

"A Christian does that every day," he said, smiling at me for a moment and then looking down at his feet, his white goatee brushing against his collar.

"Suppose I break that vow," I continued, "would that be terrible?"

"If we were perfect," said Grandpa, "we should have no need of salvation. Satan is an adversary who never sleeps. On Confirmation Sunday you vow to fight the good fight of faith."

"I think I understand," I said thoughtfully. "Why do you like to read theology books, *Bestefar*?"

"What better reading is there? What can be more interesting than trying to penetrate the ways of God and man?"

"*Bestemor*," I said, taking a deep breath and covertly watching his face, "*Bestemor* did not always read the same books as you did, *Bestefar*."

Pain like the shadow of a cloud passing swiftly over a wheat field crossed his face; then he smiled and said with a little downward tilt of his head, "Your grandmother had a simple faith unmarred by needless questioning. She was 258 one of those blessed few who believe the word of God as simply as a small child believes his parents." He sat quietly in his tall-backed rocker, his glasses lying upon his book, while tears coursed down his cheeks to the black vest below. "But isn't it time for supper?" he asked, reaching into a pocket for his handkerchief. I stroked his shoulder gently.

"We need the lights on, *Bestefar*," I said. "It's grown dark while we talked."

On Sunday morning there were seven of us kneeling on the red plush carpeting at the altar rail. Janice Saylor's face, with its upturned, provocative nose and black-lashed blue eyes, regarded the Reverend Kjelland trustingly; Faith Schlegal's brown eyes stared fixedly at her arms folded upon the altar railing. Selma's boy Norman, usually most mischievous when the occasion was solemn, for once was quiet, his merry face frozen into an impenetrable expression. Freddie Eunson, kneeling beside me, twitched restlessly, while Wilfred Tweiler and Tommy Banner knelt with rigid passivity.

"Do you, Janice Eleanor Saylor, renounce the Devil, the world, and the flesh?" asked the minister, his voice deep and sonorous. Janice's piquant face looked up trustingly.

"I do," she said, lowering her glance, a small sigh escaping with her renunciation. Would I have the courage to say my words loud enough so that Grandpa with his impaired hearing could catch my words in his pew below the pulpit?

I heard Norman's clear musical voice say, "I do." Faith's renunciation was an embarrassed mumble. The minister's black robe moved nearer. "Do you, Frederick Theodore Eunson——" began the Reverend Kjelland. Where was

Grandma, I wondered suddenly—Grandma who had sent me upstairs to memorize a Catechism in two languages? Grandma, who believed that the articles of one's faith should be so indelibly carved upon heart and mind that, should our Christian land ever be overrun with barbarians, the citadel of one's convictions could never be vanquished.

The shining black shoes, under the curling hem of the black robe, moved a step closer. "Do you, Margarethe Gyda Erdahl, renounce THE DEVIL, THE WORLD, AND THE FLESH?" My hands grew clammy, my palms pressed together.

"I do," I said, and added under my breath, "so far as I am able." The minister moved on. Wilfred Tweiler, confronted by the black robe, sent me an appealing glance, as one about to submerge for the last time. After we had tasted our first communion wine and the dry wafers had melted upon our tongues, the ceremony was over. How had I lost my sense of oneness with Grandma, there in the tension and the turmoil at the altar?

Later, at Grandma Rekve's for Sunday dinner, we girls were gathered in Room 13, away from the grownups. "Gee," said Dode wistfully, "remember how we used to race up and down the long hall and into the empty storeroom and apartments?"

"Not many kids have a hall half a block long to run in!" sighed Janice, whose father's dental offices were at one end of the long hall.

"You know, I think it's sort of sad to grow up," I remarked, looking down at my white silk confirmation stockings and the pointed white pumps which had been Uncle

Thorvald's gift.

"You know what?" asked Janice pertly. "I think Helen Rekve and Reverend Kjelland are in love."

"How do you know?" asked ten-year-old Signe, popping out of the rocking chair by the window.

"Helen's awfully plump," said Janice's sister Ginger, "but isn't she beautiful?"

"She's going back to Chicago soon," said Solveig importantly. "I don't think she'd ever settle down in Grand Prairie."

"I wish Aunt Helen would always live here," dreamed Signe. "She has such pretty things in her room, and she lets me touch them, too."

"And *gorgeous* clothes!" exclaimed Solveig. "I think she has prettier clothes than anyone in Grand Prairie!"

Grandma Rekve's only daughter appeared in the doorway as though summoned by our conversation, our assurance melting like spring snow. "Are you children having fun?" she asked. Her shining brown hair was caught above the temples with two sparkling combs. She had the warm perfection of features often found in plump women; and when she smiled her teeth gleamed white and even. Her cocoa-brown eyes inventoried our noses affectionately. "Counting the guests for second table," she laughed. She looked at Janice and me for a moment. "I really think we should have made room for our confirmation girls at the first table."

"Oh no, Helen," protested Janice politely. "That wouldn't be as much fun."

"Well, we'll be calling you girls in a few minutes," said Helen, her high heels clicking across the hall. When one of the doors into Grandma Rekve's apartment had closed upon her, we all sighed as one at the thought of being grown up, beautiful, and in love.

"I don't think I'd like to be a minister's wife," said Janice. "I want someone like—oh, maybe a corporation lawyer."

"If I *had* to marry a minister," said Dode quietly, "I wouldn't really mind someone like Reverend Kjelland. He's handsome and he's intellectual."

"He's what?" demanded Signe, outclassed in age and often on the periphery of our conversation.

"Neither would I," said Ginger. "I think he's wonderful."

"You ought to marry an undertaker," laughed Solveig. "Remember how you used to take your picnic lunch to the cemetery?" We all laughed.

"I wonder how long Norman and Janice have been sweet on each other?" teased Solveig. "Gee, I was afraid Norm would do something silly up at the altar!" Solveig rolled her huge brown eyes expressively.

"Remember how Miss Norquist used to scold us in Sunday school for giggling when we sat next to Norman?" I reminisced.

"He always sang 'Father, Son, and Holy Ost!' " laughed Janice.

"What's so funny about that?" asked Signe.

"You have to know Norwegian, silly," said her sister Solveig. " 'Ost' means cheese, and it sounded like ghost to Miss Norquist's ears, and she never figured out what we were laughing at."

"I'll bet that's the only Norwegian Norman knew!" I

exclaimed importantly, having come up the long hill of Grandma's bilingual program.

Grandma Rekve's sharp brown eyes peered around the corner and snapped us to attention. "Second table, girls," she smiled. We scrambled up from the beds and went laughing down the hall.

Late into the evening Aunt Gudrun was still up at Grandma Rekve's. "Never saw such folk for wanting to be together all the time!" Grandpa had scoffed as we walked home together. I had gone home with him to do my lessons and keep him company. I lay in bed now, with the pillows propped behind my head and the reading light on.

The gusty spring wind had brought a trace of new snow, throwing it against the double panes in large damp flakes. It was a perfect night to lie in bed reading Thomas Hardy. And wasn't Dakota itself a perfect setting for Thomas Hardy's novels—North Dakota with its gust-swept plains, its lonely reaches, its simple, straightforward farm folk dependent upon the whims of weather and sky?

I put the book down beside the bed and snapped off the bed lamp. In the kitchen below the light still burned for Aunt Gudrun's return, when the last laugh had been laughed and the last coffeepot emptied. I nestled down into the chilly reaches of the sheet and felt a sense of peace, a sense of homey luxury I could find nowhere else but in this simple house at the very edge of town.

What had happened, I wondered drowsily, to keep me from feeling the glory and the dream during the confirmation service? What had kept me from feeling that my pact with Grandma had been fulfilled?

The house shook in the exploring wind; the wisp of a

rising moon shone crazily on top of a slitted cloud—and then I knew how it was with me, and the knowing made me glad. As Aunt Gudrun was made for laughter and crowds and talking, I was made for the quiet hours, when thoughts came into the living room of my mind and sat down quietly upon chairs, waiting their turn to speak. Among them sat Grandma, in the corner by the open door; and as she started to speak she smiled. I fell asleep.

26

Always Tomorrow   "Well, I don't care!" exclaimed Aunt Gudrun, as she often did when she cared most. "If Father doesn't want Larry to come here this summer it's *his* hard luck because Larry's coming anyway."

"When?" I asked, taking hold of the clean sheet which Aunt Gudrun flipped toward me. With a sinking heart I already pictured Aunt Gudrun disappearing in a mist of white tulle and flying rice.

"In July," said Aunt Gudrun proudly. She tucked the sheet under the mattress. "Suppose you finish the bed," she suggested. "I'll be late for the office if I don't hurry."

"What *has* Grandpa said about Larry's coming?" I asked.

"What does Grandpa ever say about a man who courts me? It's always, 'What does *he* want here?' " She tucked an extra bone hairpin into her braided hairdo. "If I keep on letting others live my life I'll soon be too old to ever live my own."

"Ever to live," I corrected, tossing the heavy white
264 tasseled bedspread on the bed.

"All right, ever *to*," she said. "See what I mean?" Laughter crinkles swept up from her eyes. "Can't even talk the way I want to."

"I'm sorry, Aunt Gudrun, but you did say," I apologized with the lofty arrogance of the adolescent, "that I should correct your English. That was a split infinitive."

"You do say?" She picked up her purse and hat. "You put together all the infinitives I split around here, and I'll go up to the courthouse and make our living." She sighed for a moment, studying the disarray upstairs.

"Now never mind, Aunt Gudrun, I'll take care of everything. Now that school's out I can clean all day."

"Do keep an eye on Pa," she said. "He's out hoeing those darn potatoes, and there'll be potatoes long after he's gone. Make some coffee in the middle of the morning. That'll get him in." She disappeared down the stair well.

"Good-by!" I called. When her quick steps had taken her off the sidewalk below our window I watched her walk up the path at the side of our quiet little street. There was something wonderful about Aunt Gudrun, I thought. Though she found it irksome to work for Fred these days, she started off briskly and happily every morning, as though pleasure—and not frustration—awaited her.

The long morning shadows of bordering trees penciled across the field where *Bestefar* was working. He hoed stiffly, taking sharp little jabs at the black soil, then tamping it lightly around the greening plants. Across the field Norman burst out of the back door of the Ronald Rekve house, flung himself on the seat, and pedaled off toward 265 the store on his bicycle. His mother, Selma, came out of the same door with an old hat planted squarely on her head and marched off to the vegetable garden.

Morning was in full swing in Grand Prairie. What were my sisters doing, I wondered, in the blue-gray house next to Selma's? Doing dishes while Aunt Tina puttered about tasks out in the yard? With the Northern summer so short, the outdoors called in a sweet clear voice.

But first there was work inside. I went on into Grandpa's bedroom. With Grandma gone, he had won his victory, after some fifty years, for an almost airless bedroom. I threw the window open and breathed deeply of the clear prairie air—morning air, the air of hope and vitality.

Later, down in the kitchen, it seemed so still I felt almost as if I were being watched, while I stacked the dishes in the pantry and filled the dishpan with hot water from the reservoir. Grandma's coffee grinder stood upon a shelf, its corner slightly worn where a hand had held it in a firm grasp. Would Aunt Gudrun marry Larry? Would Grandpa and I be left alone in Grand Prairie? Would my dreams of attending college go adrift, as Aunt Gudrun's dreams had broken anchor time and again to drift in a mist of longing and uncertainty? *Bestemor* had possessed the alchemy that enabled even a dull day to carry a glint of hope.

A back door flew open. "Mugs! Mugs! Are you there?" called my sister Dode.

"Washing dishes," I called from the pantry.

"We're already done," emphasized Dode, peering around the door to the pantry. She seized a cloth lying upon the cupboard. "Here, let me help you."

"You're three to do dishes at your house," I said.

"Don't you know Aunt Tina never does dishes when

we're home?" corrected Dode. "But I came to tell you the news. Dally and I are attending college together this fall!"

"Isn't she going to teach again?" I poured boiling water on the dishes stacked in the pan.

"We'd rather see her get her degree," confided Dode importantly. "And you know what?"

"What?"

"Mundy's going to let her have all his money in his savings account!"

"Mundy?" I asked with surprise. "How come?"

"Well, Uncle can hardly afford to send two of us to college at the same time, even if Dally has a little saved. And Mundy's got almost five hundred in his account. And Mundy spoke up at the breakfast table and said he'd be glad to loan—I mean to lend—Dally the money. Isn't it cute of him?" finished Dode brightly, as she stacked cups on the pantry shelf.

"It's awfully cute of Mundy, considering he's only seven."

"That's what we think," continued Dode, "because things are a little slow in the store these years. Crops, you know. Some of the farmers owe the store a lot of money."

I hung the dishpan under the pantry table. "It's going to be awfully lonesome here next winter," I said.

"Oh, I'll write often," comforted Dode, as though she were all ready to leave. "Soon you'll be going to college too."

"Maybe," I said, looking down the dim corridor of the future and seeing Grandpa grow more frail and Aunt Gud-

267 run hurrying toward a beckoning hand from the East.

"Let's not worry about that now," said Dode. "Listen here, I came down to help you. Aunt Tina said there'd be a lot to do down here, since Aunt Gudrun wants everything ready for when Larry comes. Aren't you excited, wondering what he looks like?" She hung the dish towel on a rack behind the pantry door. "Let's see now," she said, "where shall we start?"

But even with our youthful help, Aunt Gudrun spent every free evening waxing floors, washing fancy linens, and starching the ubiquitous lace curtains of the era. Nightly her sprinkling of hated freckles was given a misting of Double-strength Othine, her long copperish hair brushed until it crackled and shone like the family copper kettle brought from Norway.

I was torn between the conviction that I should despise this interloper and the natural curiosity of the female for the sight of such a romantic legend as Larry had become in our family. When the cool night wind ruffled the fresh curtains at the west window in the living room, Aunt Gudrun rested from her labors to sit at the upright piano and sing her favorite ballads and popular songs. Grandpa, reading in his pet rocking chair, stood it as long as he could; with a backward glance at Gudrun's slim corseted figure, he rolled up the paper he was reading and strode off to the stairway and bed. Yet he never tapped his cane upon the floor as he had done in the past; and when I went upstairs and tiptoed by, he was asleep. With *Bestemor's* going, did he know that he must pay a price for Aunt Gudrun's watchful care, or had her moonsick cat music—as he once called it—become a symbol of life and warmth, in this lonely house where the chief light had been extinguished?

Still, Grandpa was not at peace about Larry's coming. Often the friendly, rhythmic sound of his saw downstairs gave place to an hour of quiet; and I would sneak down the cellar steps to find *Bestefar* staring off into space, his hands often holding a block of fresh-scented wood, his brow furrowed in thought.

One summer day the train thundered in from Minneapolis; and we who waited at home (and half of Grand Prairie, probably, for few were successful at keeping secrets) wondered what manner of man would come walking down the shaded path with Aunt Gudrun. And then they came, Aunt Gudrun quieter than she had ever been in her life before, and with her a tall, slim man more sartorially perfect than was usual in Grand Prairie, a man with thoughtful brown eyes and a large compassionate smile. And I, who had planned devious methods of making him uncomfortable should I dislike him, was instantly won over.

There followed a week of picnics and parties and dinners, to many of which I was not invited, fortunately for them—who might have to glean the harvest of a lifetime of longing in a week's time. In the church on Sunday I sat beside Larry and watched his eyes light with pride as Aunt Gudrun played the hymns. Then I wondered why Aunt Gudrun could not have picked a man I might hate; for hate has a dagger thrust, but love and fear are an upraised Excalibur. Grandpa, sitting lonely and dignified several pews ahead, would have none of this man; and while he had not uttered a single impolite word, his silence had been keen and revelatory.

269   Aunt Gudrun's enchanted week passed in days of sunny

warmth and nights of stirring breezes. Late in the evening I heard their steps upon the wooden sidewalk below the window, then their voices in the living room. Was I a burden upon their thoughts, and Grandpa's existence a worn stone in their pathway?

One suddenly chilly afternoon, when massing clouds began to stir up a rainstorm, Aunt Gudrun walked with him to the yellow depot. Shortly before, he had come into the kitchen where I was stacking dishes and given me a small thin box in which lay a string of shining simulated pearls. "I am glad you are such a help to Gudrun," he said, planting a kiss upon my cheek and holding my hands for the briefest moment. I had watched them walk down the path together. What *did* I really want for them? I thought, my mind divided, my affections strangely stirred. But Grandpa, pacing up and down under the row of cotton-woods, that windy summer evening, was not perplexed by a divided mind.

"I'm glad he's gone," he said. "Perhaps our household will once again run as it should." I paced up and down with Grandpa for a while, but I could not agree with him.

While the rain skittered across the low-pitched roof above our bedroom Aunt Gudrun undressed with me. "Well, that's over," she said. "I've never felt so lonesome in my life as I do now." She unfastened a cameo pin Larry had given her as he left and studied it tenderly. "It's a real cameo," she said. "Real and good like Larry." I slipped between the cool sheets and lay there watching her.

I could not question her nor did I feel that I wanted to, this strange bemused Aunt Gudrun, studying the milky perfection of the stone lying in the palm of her hand. She placed the brooch in its satin-lined ivory box. "Ready to turn out the light?" she asked, pushing up the window sash.

"I'm ready, Aunt Gudrun," I said.

The rain tack-hammered on the roof above us and gurgled down the rain pipe. "I'm tired," said Aunt Gudrun with a long sigh.

Timidly I ventured, "Did the visit go off the way you wanted it to?" I twined my arm with hers.

"It was perfect," she said. She spoke into the rain-voiced dark: "But probably fifteen years too late."

"What do you mean, Aunt Gudrun?" I asked.

"You can see how I'm tied down," she said, "and he has a mother and sister to look after back in Pennsylvania."

"Oh," I said, wishing desperately I knew how to be more articulate.

Aunt Gudrun sighed and turned over on her side. "But that doesn't mean I'm giving up," she said. "There's always tomorrow."

27

A Little Past Four   Waiting for the church doors to open for Sunday school, I ducked my face into the fur collar of my plaid coat. "Let's go down the cellar steps and wait there," suggested Tommy Dolman.

"Well . . ." I hesitated. "I better not."

"Afraid I'll kiss you?"

"Of course not," I lied.

"Well, come on. The wind's biting this morning." Tommy's short legs moved toward the basement stair railing. "Remember when I tried to kiss you after the school party last year?" he teased.

"Yes," I admitted, "but I don't especially like to think about it."

"Don't you like me?" he persisted. My face half hidden in my steamy furs, I looked at Tommy's squat figure and smiled. Of course I didn't like him! I liked Tuffy, Dr. Whitaker's new stepson. We exchanged glances in study hall, passed notes—but Tuffy wanted girls who would go out with him; and if I *had* asked Aunt Gudrun she would have told me I was too young for dates. Not that it really mattered; for life was an untraveled highway, climbing to new plateaus of understanding and vistas of fanciful beauty.

This was the Reverend Kjelland's last Sunday in Grand Prairie. We watched him whirl his coupe around the back of the church and brake to a hasty stop at the back stairway. Who would ever take his place, speak as eloquent and beautiful English, possess the audacity to remain a man as well as a clergyman? His presence, I reflected, had helped deliver Grandma safely into another world and had given *Bestefar* many coveted hours of reading and discussion.

"Well, you're safe. The church door is open," scoffed Tommy with disgust, following me up the concrete steps to the oak doors. After Sunday school the church began to fill rapidly, even with strangers who had never been there before and probably would never come again.

"After all our worries," whispered Janice to Solveig and me, "he's still single." We crowded together in a rear pew. Aunt Gudrun's swelling prelude terminated our whispering, and the service began. When the minister turned to the altar and began to chant for the last time in his clear, deep baritone, "Glory be to God in the highest," and the congregation sang in return, "And on earth peace, good will toward men," many eyes were filled with tears.

When he ascended his pulpit for the last time and delivered a sermon of challenge and hope, the people sat almost as one; and when the collection plates were passed, even those with "a purse within a purse," as Uncle Thorvald once described a miserly farmer's giving, gave generously. At the very end of the service when all sang, "Blest be the tie that binds our hearts in human love," many were weeping openly. So the Reverend Kjelland went to a bigger call far away, and the white frame church near the north end of Main Street must wait for a new pastor; but to some of us who had knelt there to make a vow or receive a sacrament or had come in to say farewell to those who had journeyed beyond our sight and understanding, the church would never seem the same again.

In school, having satisfied the two-year mathematics requirements, I was able to abandon myself to the joy of learning. Miss Bauer, teaching us composition and literature, also taught us to honor words as the sound of the human race in its slow ascent up the ladder of knowledge. Sitting upstairs in the study hall, the furnace registers hissing their eternal battle against the outside cold, I often dreamed across the rooftops of Grand Prairie, saw the wheat fields sleeping under layers of blown snow, looked at the bare branches of elms and cottonwoods waiting stiffly for the sure return of spring. In the subzero cold the smoke rose from the house chimneys in an arrowed line.

273 I loved them all, all eight hundred in Grand Prairie, the

babies, the children, the mothers and the fathers, and the old treading their slow, bent way across the swollen, hard-packed snow; and if I were ever hurt, the pain lasted but a day. These were my people; and when we walked home from glee club in the early winter twilight of a January evening the lights from their windows shone warmly upon the heaped snow; and down in the little hollow where the willow branches cracked in the increasing cold, the light from our kitchen window cast a golden square upon the clean snow and the smoke from Grandpa's chimneys rose in a straight black line.

"Well, I quit my job," said Aunt Gudrun after I had placed my overshoes back of the kitchen range. "I can hardly believe it myself, but I've quit."

"You did decide to run in the primaries this spring!" I exulted, grabbing hold of Gudrun's firmly corseted but slender waist.

"Now don't get so excited!" disparaged Aunt Gudrun. "It doesn't pay to get your hopes too high."

Grandpa stood in the doorway to the living room. "*Ja*," he said thoughtfully, "the first politician our family has produced is a woman."

"Well, why not?" asked Aunt Gudrun as she turned over a simmering Swiss steak.

"I have not criticized," said Grandpa. "I have but remarked."

Gudrun shook out a clean white tablecloth and pulled it across the oval table. "Do you think I have a chance, Father?"

"*Det ved jeg intet*," he said, shaking his head. "That I 274 don't know. You can but try." He reached for the plates

I had put on the table and put them around at our places. When he rose from his work he leaned heavily upon his cane.

"How do you feel, *Bestefar?*" I asked, rubbing my cold cheek against his stubbly beard.

"*Bare godt,* just so-so," he replied.

You belong in Tucson, you're getting so crippled," worried Gudrun as she dished up the vegetables.

"Next winter, perhaps," he said. "That is, unless we have a woman county clerk of court."

Gudrun sat down, and we bent our heads in prayer. She looked up soon, worrying. "Perhaps I shouldn't have done it. I might be making it difficult for all of us. I've been promised little jobs up at the courthouse in one office or another between electioneering stints. Still, I'll have to be away from home a lot," she mused.

"If the door is left open, snow *will* drift in," remarked Grandpa. "We shall make out. You will see." He buttered his bread slowly. "But I would advise you not to set your heart upon it. There will be some who will not vote for you because you are a woman, and there will be many who will vote for a veteran—a disabled veteran, at that—even though he has a private income with his farm."

"That's just it!" flared Gudrun. "He doesn't need it like I do!"

"*Kanske,* perhaps," conceded Grandpa. "But logic has rarely marked a ballot. Nor can you forget the German votes, and the Germans carry much weight in parts of our county."

"Oh, *Far!*" exclaimed Gudrun. "You make me feel bad already that I've quit my job!"

The clock struck six, taking long whirring breaths between each resounding gong. "I am not predicting your defeat," he reasoned, "only suggesting that you prepare for a battle." He smiled. "And of all the three girls I fathered, you are best fitted for such a battle."

When the primaries were over and Aunt Gudrun was finally in the race, it was easy to see that she did have a battle on her hands, as Grandpa had predicted. Borrowing Uncle Sven's car, she made every township that summer, often taking little Mundy along for company as she started off to the hills in the south of the county or up to the fertile farms north and east of the county seat.

"Promises! Promises and arguments, that's all I've heard all summer!" exclaimed Gudrun as the harvest days moved toward fall. My sisters were in college, and in another year's time I, too, should know whether college were in the plans for me. Fall rains splashed at the raw black plains. The geese swooped down upon the harvested fields and gleaned the leavings, rose on whirring wings, and melted, arrow-formed, into the night. Down in the basement *Bestefar* sat at his carpenter bench and fashioned himself crutches so that he might go about the house and tend to the furnace and kitchen range in our absence. With the coming of the first snow, Aunt Gudrun settled down to await the election. "I don't think I've missed a farm!" she exclaimed. "You know, there are Germans who have never forgiven me for serving on the draft board during the war, and calling their boys to fight against the mother country." She poured the heavy Weidnar cream from Grandma's delft blue pitcher into her waiting coffee.

276   "Don't wear yourself out thinking of the votes you

might have gained or lost. The silent ballot will speak loud enough," advised Grandpa.

"And there are some who say I should never have run against a veteran," continued Gudrun, so pale with weariness that the freckles against which she waged a nightly battle had receded into slumber.

A week later we sat in the living room after supper. "Well, at least it's over!" sighed Gudrun, fingering through her music in the stand beside the piano. "Harvey Blayne was probably right. If I had run for any other office in the courthouse I might have won."

"Count yourself lucky you lost!" scoffed Uncle Sven, his feet propped inelegantly upon the settee which housed the furnace register. "What do you want a political office for? Can't you find enough grief in this world without playing hand-maiden to the fickle public?"

"I thought you were going to guarantee your precinct!" taunted Gudrun with a good-natured laugh.

"I thought so too," admitted Uncle Sven ruefully. "Couldn't penetrate that strong Teutonic bloc up north of us." Uncle Sven poured tobacco into his pipe. "Got a lot of pre-election promises out of them."

"The word of a man you drink beer with is often forgotten when the stein is empty," put in Grandpa.

Aunt Gudrun sat down on the round piano stool and fingered the keys absently. "It was all my fault, thinking I deserved a public office."

"Ha!" scorned Uncle Sven. "You almost got it." He shrugged his shoulder. "Now where would you be if you had won? Electioneering every election time. Stuck in the
same groove until you die. If you're sensible you'll forget

all this nonsense and do what Henry wants you to do. Take Father and go to Tucson. What in heaven's name is there to keep you up here?"

"I hope we stay here forever!" I exclaimed loyally.

"Well, it might mean college for you next year," said Aunt Gudrun soberly. "The university's there, you know. In fact it might be the only way you can ever get to college." We said nothing, listening to the rising wind make its forays around the house, shaking the shutters on the porch beside the living room. "But it's *Far* we must think about," said Gudrun, her eyes looking toward Grandpa nodding in his chair, his glasses resting on a book upon his lap. "Last year he was so stiff he could scarcely get out of bed; and this year he drags his way about the house on crutches. It's lonesome for him when we're away, you know that."

"Go!" urged Uncle Sven, swinging his warmed-up legs from the furnace settee. "There's nothing left for you here. Write Henry you're coming."

So it was like Aunt Gudrun, once the matter was settled, to make her plans quickly, and even to talk as if she could not leave soon enough. "Maybe I've been a fool to stay this long!" she said one afternoon when I found her in the cellar, sorting castoffs that write the silent history of every family gathered under a roof.

"What are you going to do with this?" I asked, going to a corner under a cellar window where an ancient cobwebbed chest reposed under its mantle of powdered dust.

"You mean your grandmother's wedding chest? That 278 was her dowry chest," she explained, as though I did not

Guro
Gullicks
Datter
Bjotveit

know. Inscribed upon the front panel under the heavy hand-hammered lock were the words "Guro Gullicksdatter Bjotveit." My fingers traced the faded scrolled lettering. "Guro, the daughter of Gullick of Bjotveit," I said.

Gudrun picked up an ancient book smelling sharply of mildewed leather. "I had almost forgotten we had this!" she exclaimed. "It's the *Pilgrim's Progress*, translated into the Norwegian. Why, it's over 105 years old!" The browned pages began to crackle and disintegrate in her hands as she held them.

"I'm going upstairs. I'll make supper," I said quickly. So that was the stuff of which life was made! I thought wistfully as I filled the teakettle and put it forward on the range. Once *Bestemor* had been as young as I, with heavy brown braids falling to her bosom, her gray eyes sparkling with verve and life. We had a picture of *Bestefar* in his Norwegian army uniform, and he stood six feet two, broad-shouldered and straight, and not even a photograph could hide the twinkle in his eyes, the amused smile on his face. "When we were first married," Grandma had once said, "your grandfather liked to play at cards and drink ale late into the night as many of the young men did. I could not have it, for I was heavy with child and I knew surely there were more to come. For us such habits would have ended in family ruin."

"What did you do, *Bestemor*?" I innocently asked.

"I only said he might have either—I at home to be his wife or he at cards and drink."

I remember how Grandma's tired shoulders had lifted as she spoke and how the faraway look in her eyes stared 280 across the passage of years with tender pride. "And when he made his choice, and I am certain he did at that very moment, I needed never to question his coming or going again; for he was always a man who kept his word and knew his own mind."

I put Grandpa's evil-smelling jar of *Gammelost*, literally "old cheese," upon the table beside his plate. If we could just once, I thought, lift the dusty draperies of time and look back into the years. What would one see? Two young people, one tall and straight and fair, the other small and dark and gentle, standing beside the fjord's edge and pointing to the place where the quiet and deep waters met the turbulent North Sea, and onward to another land? And yet the pointing hand which was directed to the promise of tomorrow must irrevocably come to such a room as the one below the house where Gudrun now toiled, where the ancient wood of a bride's chest shone wraithlike in the winter gloom, the lovely *rose-maling* of the once bright scrollwork faded like the face of one once comely. It was as *Bestemor* had often said: nothing in the human scene ever lived but the spirit, and who would love the flesh except as the fragile receptacle of the soul?

"Look what I've brought up for Aunt Tina!" exclaimed Gudrun, coming into the kitchen.

"Oh, the old copper kettle," I said, my thoughts still bemused.

"It has that narrow base so that it can fit down into the hole where the lid rested—heats faster," explained Gudrun. "We used it that way, many times when I was small," she said.

"We're taking the clock, aren't we?" I asked.

281 "I'm afraid not. Afraid it'll never stand the journey."

"*Bestemor* often said when I was small it might even tick away the hours in my own kitchen."

"Forget it," advised Gudrun. "I'm tired, and your Aunt Tina grew up with the sound of it too. Let it tick in her kitchen. She'll be lonely enough with all of us gone."

I placed the chairs around the table. "Oh, that's all right," I said, "for no matter where I am I'll hear it forever."

Aunt Gudrun wiped her hands on the roller towel above the sink, giving me a strange, scowling look. "What a queer girl you are at times!" she exclaimed. "I'll be darned if you don't act as if every other thing in the world is alive!"

So even before we were ready to quit it, the house grew empty and strange and seemed to taunt us with its sudden desertion. Upstairs in the old bell-towered schoolhouse I often sat with tear-filled eyes, for when again would learning ever seem so sweet or warm red desks, marked by iniquitous carvings, speak more eloquently of friendships carried through the years?

Mrs. Weidnar served us "cabbage bungles" once again; and across the street in the Tweiler house I sat beside a bed and listened to a neighbor say, "I never did sell a story— not a single story in all these years. It's too late now. Mr. Tweiler says I'll be up soon, but I know better."

In the Rogby house a cherry rocker moved forth and back more slowly. "Sven has started to church again," she said. "But for me nothing has changed. The world is still often soiled and evil, and if there is anyone about who cares to remedy it, I have never met him." And when I

282 walked through November snows to call upon another

Zemke cow, a new street light at the end of our lane swung cheerily back and forth. It's years too late, I thought, welcome as the light was; for the specters that had hovered there in earlier years had almost fled. For what had they been but tired people with their work all done, as we ourselves had lain to rest one grown too tired for toil?

Then one afternoon when the gray sky overhead seemed to sag with its burden of undropped snow, *Bestefar* turned the key in the lock of the back door and we went across the hard-frozen field to Aunt Tina's once more, where the old clock made an alien but homing sound in her modern kitchen. They were all there, as our family always was, given any proper excuse: Grandma Rekve, arrow-straight and proud, and Selma with her ready talk and smile. The Rekve brothers sat in the living room puffing on their cigars, as I had always remembered them to do. Anna Norquist, who had been one of us ever since she had taken an apartment above the Rekve Store, came by with a gift in her hand, and I remembered what *Bestefar* had once said about her: "That woman would find a good trait even in the Devil." When the hour came to leave, Aunt Tina said in a voice all tight, "I won't go down to the depot to see you off. I can't do it. I'll say good-by here."

At the little yellow depot Uncle Sven stood waiting on the windy platform. "I'm glad you got away to say good-by!" exclaimed Gudrun, looking relieved, for she must always have around those she loved.

"I'm going too!" he laughed.

"You can't! Your job, why——" Aunt Gudrun's face grew sober with dismay.

"Job be hanged!" Uncle Sven laughed. "There are more

jobs in Tucson than in the whole state of North Dakota!"

In the little waiting room beside the potbellied stove, Gudrun turned to Uncle Thorvald. "He can't go! I hadn't planned it, for him to come too."

"I know," said Uncle Thorvald with his big gentle smile. "It has always been that way for you. You've never been free of those who need you."

In the windy, late afternoon gloom outside the yellow depot, the coffee train whistled throatily at the cemetery crossing, its old familiar voice lost for a moment on the wind. Then its headlight shone as the train rounded a curve and raced toward us through the whirling snow.

Grandpa, steadied by Uncle Thorvald's hand, shuffled forward on his crutches. The locomotive shook the high wooden platform under our feet and the red coaches clattered to a screeching stop. The porter put the stool down at Grandpa's feet and grasped him firmly by the arm. "Mister, this place sure is cold!" he exclaimed.

When we were all on, we looked down at the faces of Uncle Thorvald and Mundy and all the rest who had come down to say good-by, holding their collars up against the northwest wind and waving their mittened hands. The train lurched, the whistle blew; and soon we were gliding past the tall grain elevators and the courthouse, where blinking lights shone from the windows and fought the winter gloom.

The coffee train whistled sharply at the last almost obscured crossing in town. I pressed my face against the cold windowpane and looked out into the darkening night. This was the train, I thought, this train whistling even now, that had come a little past four o'clock for more times than I could remember and had caused a hundred coffeepots to find their way to the front of crackling ranges. But only Grandma had thought to call it "the coffee train." Above the noisy rhythmic clacking of the wheels I seemed to hear her words again. "Put on the coffeepot, my little one, the coffee train is here."